THE SAINT (

THE SAINT OF SODOMY

AND OTHER WORKS

§§

Verse by

William Tarvin

GLB PUBLISHERS ®   San Francisco

FIRST EDITION

Published in the United States by
GLB Publishers
P.O. Box 78212, San Francisco, CA 94107 USA

Cover by W. L. Warner

Library of Congress Catalog Card Number:

99-60416

ISBN 1-879194-27-9

First printing   April, 1999
10 9 8 7 6 5 4 3 2 1

CONTENTS

THE SAINT OF SODOMY 3

PORTRAIT OF A STATUE
      AS A (VERY) YOUNG MAN . . . 73

UPON SHAKESPEARE'S COUCH 109

AN ANTI-ELEGY FOR AUDEN 123

BIOGRAPHICAL NOTE 127

THE SAINT OF SODOMY

Don Jaunt felt ill and overwhelmed by all
He had been through. "Now this!" His sigh grew frantic
As the intercom staticked, "No alcohol
. . . Arabia," words sobering each transatlantic
New York-Jeddah pilgrim, and casting a pall
That drove Don's mere depressive into the manic.
Fate stared at him, in the obtuse shape of a casaba:
"I soon shall be in the land of the blackest Black Kaa'ba."

The jet touched down; a dazed Don left the plane in
Darkness, shoved down an uterine stairway
To macadam. "Is nothing allowed to remain in
Its cherished womb?" he pondered. "Is the fairway
Ever fair?": the question next to hold co-reign in
His mind, now grounded after fourteen airway
Hours. He looked around. "Where is the terminus?"
A third sad thought, as he boarded the shuttle bus.

While he moves through this and that slow airport line,
Let's take in Don, our Epyllion's gallant.
He's 36, accepts his youth's decline,
Wears orthopedic shoes, and holds askant
His sagging stature; his crewcut blond hairline
Is graying. Looks unheroic, I grant—
Except in height (midway between Napoleon's 5' 6",
And Nelson's 5')—but soon you'll marvel at his heroics.

The Arab woman ahead looked like a Rorschach,
Black enigmaed in her *abaaya* from head to toe.
"A breathing, breeding mummy." Don's mind drew back,
Having used that final word, *non comme il faut*.
"'Twas I, not she, who's driven me to this whore-shack
Of a country." The customs line, more stop than go,
Inched forward. Don strove with firmness not to eye the handsome
Checker. "To do so I'd have to undo myself, aye, and some

Other things about me." His thoughts continued on
As stark confession. "His moustache, acreage
To swoon me." (Now it's out: No pale paragon,
El-Cidic, or from some Virgilian page
A mannequinish mirror is our Don.
Rather a gay, reared in a closeted age
Where Artifice reigned—O Muse, make my words so lyric,
That all who read will judge Don's epic as Homeric!)

After that (enclosed in parentheses) on
Don Jaunt's *arcite*, next know he held within
His dreams of the manly body with more of less on.
He paused to eye the male garb Arabian:
"Surely I can't desire a man with a dress on!"
He hoped, still gripped by what Society termed Sin.
(*Thobes*, they're called, the long white robes that bedeck them.)
"But the thin cloth shows each crotch!" Despite his throes to
       check them,

Don's eyes shot round like sparks from a fiery volcano
As he found a terminal seat, all bones a-weary,
Save one. "Cease! Too toward a glance and all can know

What I am, . . . but each seems hung as the dromedary
This country's noted for, not a weak-kneed soprano
Among the lot," he marked, and quickly cursed his dreary
Fate: "Only the fallen, the depth of the fall can know."
With that he slipped into sleep, his thoughts tortured and eerie.

For 600 lines or so let us leave
Our airport-stranded hero to reverie.
Too soon mayhap he'll wake to find a sleeve,
Drool-smeared, a nose that works too well, one eye
Mattered, the other beyond handkerchief,
And head to the toilet, seeking reality.
For now, we let him slumber, sleeping off his dose
Of jetlag. (But, Reader, you're not allowed to doze.)

Don's sleep is well-deserved, but you and I
"Must post o'er land and ocean without rest"
To find what brought Don Jaunt to this strand. I
Began *in medias res* (acknowledged best
By all but Byron), and dropped him in sandy
Saudi Arabia, but what's our hero's "quest"?
To answer that grave query, I think it may be an
Apt time to delve into his life pre-Arabian.

When he was yet but *Ur*-Don, Donna Jones
(Nee Bellow), mother-to-be, settled first
Her married name was common as cow bones;
"Of all tags in this world ours is the worst;
My son should have a family *nomen* he owns
Alone, distinctive as a comet's thrust,"
She shrieked at Husband Bob in bed. "Lower the damn range
Of your voice"—his coitus spoiled—"You'll have your name
        change."

Next day she dabbed a new pen in a new inkwell.
"He'll excel all others:" so "Jones" became "Giant."
"But such Titans [sic] were brutes, and I don't think, well,
They were the best lovers, nor that self-reliant,
Like Byron's Don Juan. Now doesn't that link well?
Fits to a 't.' Yes, he'll be dubbed Don Jaunt!"
Bob thought the "'culiar moniker" might queer the kid,
But had learned you give in, to get in, when wed.

So much for Donna's first machination.
The second's known, if you were somewhat attentive
To the stanza-preceding's overt ambulation.
If not, return to it. . . . Now all retentive,
You know her mettle was Macbethian
(The Lady, of course) and struck with her incentive.
Donna did not care if 'twere an ill or a well child,
But by Heavens' hags, hers had to be a male-child.

She did not care if 'twere a swarthy or pale child,
   "   "   "   "   "   "   " bane or a bale child,
   "   "   "   "   "   "   " *vale* or all-hail child,
But by Heavens' hags, it had to be a male-child.
She did not care if 'twere a shy or kiss/tell child,
   "   "   "   "   "   "   " *haut* or wholesale child.
It could be a C.O.D. or regular mail child,
But by Heavens' hags, it had to be a male-child.

She did not care if 'twere a sighted or Braille child,
   "   "   "   "   "   "   " sickly or hale child,
   "   "   "   "   "   "   " fat or thin-as-a-rail child,
But by Heavens' hags, it had to be a male-child.

She did not care if 'twere a scented or stale child,
"   "   "   "   "   "   " scrimping or prodigal child,
It could cuddle or be a hard-as-a-nail child,
But by Heavens' hags, it had to be a male-child.

Each day she clutched her swell while intoning,
"Son, son," convinced her sway and chords were tonic
Sol-fa, dispelling any feminine cloning.
She believed the myth the masculine Ionic
Columnists were inspired by the sensual moaning
Of Graecian maids whose song was telephonic,
And all the glory of each grand Greek erection
Was the climax of a symphonic connection.

"No daughter," her mutter, "to muddy the water.
"   "   , a squatter, pissing like an otter.
"   "   , whose father treats her as a bother,
And like the mother deep down sought the other.
No daughter whose birth or upbringing have worth or
Design should th'other not take her to altar."
As a rib, unspared, Donna sobbed but continued on,
Speaking more to herself than to her venued son.

"No daughter," her mutter, "to be wed to her better,
"   "   , acceptor of hell and of halter,
"   "   , a waiter, whom th'other can alter
And solder and mold her because he's the holder.
No daughter doomed to loiter while he gets it harder,
Who must worship and be sacrificed at the selfsame altar."
Donna knew—How she knew!—a girl must be so and do so,
And was no mo' than she brought with her trousseau.

She clutched her belly (How she did carry on!),
Listing the sufferings of her sex without stint.
Her survey showed that of all men, aye, nary one
Had sustained such sorrow as those all-descendent
Of Eve. She screamed, grasping, "Let this be carrion,
Stillborn, if a male-child to be isn't meant."
O reader, you now see when one gets fanatical,
One likely will lapse into the ungrammatical.

Surely Donna would have said without contortion,
"Stillborn, if a male-child isn't meant to be,"
Had Hysteria Precox not caused *hysteron*
Cum proteron—a vile hysterotomy
In syntax. (I insert this lest me the censure on
You put, and say I like rhyme, o'er mused poetry.
In truth whene'er either females or males storm
What is vented is a vulgar priscian maelstrom.)

But back to Donna, whose all-tiresome /al/-/ild/
Had returned (she having miscarriaged every daughter
E'er born): "No care be he hellion or Holy Grail Child,"
Etc., she intoned, between sips of soda water
And sermonettes on Christ's having been a male-child,
And Moses too. "Had the Pharaonic slaughter
Been led by me, I'd have urged the soldierly men,
'Massacre the female, but spare the masculine.'"

The day came: Donna in her lotus position,
Oblivious, her psyche, epi-stable,
Was fixed on the word, "son," "son," "son," "son," "son,"
When out squirted Don onto the cold kitchen table,

Slid along its hard comfort and o'erran
The edge. There he dangled from his uterine cable,
Until Donna awoke from the trance she was dim in.
Grogg'ly, she grasped the cord, and started reeling him in.

Though Donna wasn't much at cleaning house,
You'd have thought she liked all things immaculate,
The way she tore into that placental mess
And grappled with the slimy precipitate,
But all her frenzy was not to the baby's face
Directed; she scratched at that portion mediate.
Her fingernails frustrated, with her teeth she bit the heinous
Goo away, then hallelujahed: Her Don had a penis!

Two hours later, Bob came home and found
Mother and son near dead on the cold hardtop.
The poor baby, though still umbilicus-bound,
Had somehow shaken off its natal slop,
And crawled toward a breast. Donna's own right hand
Had not relinquished; it still lay atop
The baby's—Bob turned away from this sight with shock
But, Reader, I won't turn; I'll call a cock a cock.

"Never once grabbed mine that way," Bob let sigh
As he dialed 911. That Don did survive
Already you know, but not, "Did Donna die?"
Early death's a staple in the narrative
Heroic, a loss an epicist should sure comply
With. What better way to keep death alive,
Furiously driving our Don from one quest to another,
Than the Orestal memory that he'd killed his mother.

But Donna wasn't one who cared for tradition.
She wasn't about to croak at that glad moment
When all her dreams had come to their fruition.
(For sure the lady did not know what "No" meant.)
The medics arrived and hurried to their mission
To find, in truth, she kenned not what "Let go" meant.
They tried this way, that way, but made such poor gain,
For nothing could loosen her hold on Don's wee organ.

O! such determination is the great stuff of
What dreams, not death, are made. This lady who'd
All-unnerved sex was not about to slough off
Her mortal coils in tragic attitude.
I hope, O Reader, you haven't had enough of
The mother of Don, for she won't be subdued.
She's wrecking my epic, but—Ye Muse!—what can I do?
If a lady can launch, *certes* she can cause to lie to

A thousand ships (or a saga), or she's no woman.
For Donna, minor was prelude to major:
Her Don was male-born, but he was yet no man.
So Donna with herself made a third wager:
The name in ink, the blood of womb, the omen
Of the third, fire. She would become Don's saggar
And forge a man of fabled masculinity.
The divine spark must catch, she knew, in the nursery.

If dress does make the man, then 'tis decor
Will mold the manly: This was Donna's *logos*.
Don's nursery must house no fie-fay color
Of teal or peach or toki, or other bogus

Temperas, pastels, where pale has turned to paler.
An emphatic Donna declared these to be no-go's.
(Her befuddled painter did wonder, "What did—uh—she mean
By asking if I had pigments enriched with semen?")

Rather, the nursery's ceiling was all gamboge
As if the sun had loosened a great flare.
The walls' primeval vert recalled an age
Which did not rust its forests, *laissez-faire*,
With The Modern Rain of squandered appanage.
For the panels, the umber of earthenware.
The season-based tones of loam and fire and greenery:
These were the rudiments of male–affinity,

Or so Donna reasoned. And on the walls,
She put no playful bunnies, chirping birds,
Nor frogs attired in hats and overalls,
No Muffet dining on her whey and curds,
No Jack and giant drawn sans cocks and balls,
No cows in cow fields minus the cow turds.
No limp limnings of the lion lying with the lamb.
Instead she tacked up battle posters of Vietnam:

Of this legionnaire tossing a hand grenade,
Of that one nestled next to his fav'rite gun.
And glosses of musclemen who did parade
The ideal stuff 'tween skin and skeleton;
Manly magnates with the look of the self-made
Who showed the race was both hard-run and -won.
And Donna taped o'er the nursery's window pane
A larger-than-life cut-out of the great John Wayne,

With "three" guns blazing! As for tot toys
There were none. (And so, O Reader, you're spared
Another of my pet rhetorical ploys—
Not this, but that. Still I reserve that card
For later play, so please constrain your joys.)
Donna deemed the joys of toys a wry canard
Half-sold by Spock and the other docs of that stipple:
The only toy a male-babe needed was a nipple.

And so the next of Donna's maw-maw dilemmas:
Her spawning was her bliss, but—O!—her breasts,
Her pride. More lofty than an analemma's
Burst, they were her sex's sole unsunken crests,
And should they suffer the worst of anathemas,
The babe's gnaw-claw, would not her Everests
Erode, shrivel, collapse? And yet she feared she'd lose 'im,
If she denied her Don free access to her bosom.

When desperate, Donna was like a J. Caesar
Who came to conquer, not just to see.
The Rubicon was there *not* to cross her,
But to be crossed. Her thoughts did finally
Settle on what she came to term a "tit-teaser,"
A bra o'erbuilt her breasts, her dairy–to–be.
From baby bottles to bra's nips, she ran two tubes,
Enema-like. A squirt would send to the latex boobs

A stream of formulaed milk ("A wassail-cup,"
She called the flow). But would this make-believe
Ensnare? She drew the newborn babe to his sup,
Hoping that Moses–like he'd deign receive.

He sucked—she squeezed—and soon was lapping up
That which the sly woman had up her sleeve.
And did Don take in with the milk the cunning web
That Eve–struck women weave for more than baby's neb?

(That's my, not Donna's, abashed conundrum.)
Her breasts preserved in color, shape, and texture,
She lay back, the problem of pabulum
Resolved, and spied while Don with ambidexter
Kneaded each falsie, while "the trues" stayed numb.
But watching brought a startling new conjecture:
"A robust newborn male should be all head and prick:
Sans doute, Don's head is large, but the other's just a nick!

... Is this a portent?" Donna yerked with fright,
For since that Labor Day's struggle, not any
Thought had she given to how well bedight
Her Don was. In truth, nonplused by Bob's many
Cruel jokes, she had from natal day averted sight
From what she saw now was "no mor'an a penny.
Will my poor baby—Darling Don—be such a po'man,
Having no mo' downstairs than a clitoric woman?"

She jumped up, tearing loose that arch contraption
Mammalian, and ran about the room,
Flinging her arms (and tubes) in each direction,
Oblivious to the wails of Don, the victim
Of lacto-globular interruption.
"I've got to find out where this curse came from.
I've got to know if coming years will self-correct it,
That paltry thing nativity has scarce erected."

(Desist, Donna, Miltonically I plead.
Do not seek to disturb this natal Eden.
Accept that some knowledge cannot be treed,
And if you dig at one root, it will lead on
To another, until the whole tree is destroyed.
But did she listen? To find out, please read on.)
Straightaway, she dialed her Bob. "I'd rate your cock an 'Egads!'"
She began. "Now what about your dad's and your granddad's?"

After two years of marriage to his Donna,
Nothing she did or said could rattle Bob:
"From Dad's—May he rest in peace!—springald ana
Comes this tale of the first day when for hobnob
He called upon that fixtured whore Miss Lana,
Who eying his grand thing started to sob
And swore she ne'er had spied a thing so splendid as
His tool, unless it was the ramrod of my granddad's!"

"That leaves my side." Donna dropped the black receiver
With a sigh. "An only child, I have no brother
To tell me gladly all 'bout his upheaver . . .
And worms don't talk . . . . I guess there is no other
Way," though Donna would've preferred to leave her
Out of all this. She dialed. "Is that you, mother?
Hello, Momma, this is Donna, yes, yes, your daughter.
I need to know: 'Did Daddy have a big—uh—flyswatter?'"

The phone slammed down. "She's probably too embarr'ssed,"
Donna mulled, "to admit, poor thing, she doesn't know.
Likely closed her eyes when Daddy undressed
And let her mind drift when he did his do."

Now Donna, ere she let Bob's cock congest
Her hole, did microscope it both high and low.
For her, foreplay was fraught with philosophic forethought,
And there was more to the bed than any whore thought.

"No problem, not when old Doc Downs's a dear."
She dialed. "Dad knew and trusted his physic—
No other's—from birth to burst" (a stroke last year).
"Surely some time 'twixt nick and prick and stick
He saw Dad's—" A "Hello." "Doc Downs, Donna here.
Was Daddy decked with a ding-dong of a dick?" . . .
"The lengthy silence means he's checking," Donna surmised,
And then that selfsame click. She was and wasn't surprised.

"Now'days doctors discard all records before
The corpse is cold. In that they're like family.
(E.g., my dial on Dad to the Goodwill Store
Was pre-funereal.) No help to me,
Doc Downs," she moaned. "And my Don, th'inheritor
Perchance of a largesse that'll ne'er pass a pea
In size. The torment, Oh!" She railed at her family root,
Cocksure it could produce only low-lying fruit.

But Donna was plucky (That, you certainly know).
She bounced back, jumped up, did two dervish spins,
Then spoke: "When mothers/doctors lie or lie low,
I'll sniff the truth through Daddy's manly sins,
Which from the gab I've heard were quite *de trop*."
How her odyssey led to the Wexler twins
Needs no detailing. Suffice to say, she had to do some
Canvassing—like Ulysses—ere striking on that twosome.

These two old maids of their old neighborhood
Like all its other ladies (the men she'd planned
For later) greeted her with a smiling "Good
Day, Donna," and a taking of her hand.
Unlike the others who were, she thought, quite rude
When, "pleasants" over, they'd come to understand
Why Donna had called to correspond, each Wexler matron
Grinned, giggled, then proceeded to elaborate on.

"Now we were virgins," Wilhelmina began—
"We were, we are," Wisteria with an emphatic
Hiccup aventred— "that day your dad crawled in
Through yon window and coaxed us to the attic—"
"Spouting off about how *original* sin
Is and that we should join in the general traffic."
"We were but girls of fifteen"— "but feisty"— "prone to gossip."
"But whether we would give in, that was a toss-up."

"We did," It was Wilhelmina's confession.
"Oh yes, we did," (Wisteria), "we did, we did."
"Among the attic's toys we gave accession.
As for your dad, he did—well—what he did."
"Oh yes, he did" (*op. cit.*). "But penetration,
No." "No penetration" (*op. cit.*, sadly she did
Echo.) Donna's fears expressed themselves in a snort:
"He couldn't break your foreskin! Was his cock so short?

Was Daddy's such a runt-sized pee-shooter?
(And my poor Don has got the selfsame gene!)"
The Wexlers twittered. "Willah, you must refute her
Asap, who libels the manliest cock ever seen!"

"Oh, Donna, do you think your dad a neuter?"
"He had no pea—" "More the stalk of Jack's bean."
"You see we're ladies of the old-timey generation."
"Between the legs we took it." "But no penetration."

"His cock was longer than a ladies' longing."
"And broader than the broad side of a barn."
"Tell, Sister, how her dad did his ding-donging.
You'll find it most economical, the yarn."
"He did not do us in the way ping-ponging
Or where we each would get a solitaire turn,
But packed us side-by-side, and slid his cock heigh-ho"—
"Oh yes, it was at least a duodecimo!"—

"If I was in the front, my mossy substance
Would firstly feel the fire of that fast friction.
He'd pause and jiggle it—" "Oh such a dance!"—
"Then slither it 'cross the hole of my execration—"
"Her ass hole, dear."— "The journey of his lance
But half-done, Wisteria will tell how he thrust on."
It dawned on Donna: "Dad disdained to waste his hard-ons,
But stacked them, racked them, packed them, fucked them like
        sardines."

"From Wilhelmina's ass-dump, like a comet,
His head came at my cunt in comet's flight,
Grazed 'gainst my grass, and having taken from it,
Continued, leaving me in Dido's plight
When Aeneas ran off in search of Rome. (At
The least, the Lady had one fiery night.)
On sailed his cock, on past the stenching whirling pool
Of my full-farting furnace, and came forth like a bull—"

"You mean aft' having had four holes in one,"
A gasping Donna murmured, "still his cock's head
"Protruded—" Wist: "Like a red apple on
A hung branch—" "Or a brooch, in shape an ox-head,
Dangling from a thick chain of gold, pure-spun."
"All this is true or call my cunt a pox-head."
But Donna cared no fig for the health of their vaginas:
She was so happy she laughed like a pack of hyenas.

Right then to Venus she vowed she would no more
Mull o'er the mass of her Don's under-massing.
She was reliant in time it would grow more
And more 'til it would be a thing surpassing
All others. The Wexlers were pulsed to a-crow more
About their puberty's full overpassing,
But Donna demurred. She'd had her fill of the splendor
"Of ladies who pant to paean—pee on—like Pindar."

As down she walked the pathway from the Wexler
Mansion, Donna thought back to when she was three;
Her daddy used to slide a knee betwixt her
Legs, then lift her to his lap so playfully,
And bounce her up and down. It used to perplex her
How his soft lap turned harder with each spree.
Her childish wish: "Is apple there for me, or locket?"
But now she knew, "the darkness hidden in his pocket."

Poor Donna started retching on the lawn,
The Wexler lawn. (I've hinted truth is gruesome,
Less sulliedly solid than an Archimedean
"*Eureka*," more like Lot's seeds.) "We must do some

Something," Wist said, but looking found Donna gone,
And gone her childhood saints also. A new sum
Now she tallied. Belly empty, her mind was full,
Of the flotsam and jetsam of the subtle sexual.

"The man is more than father of the child;
And the child is more than fathered by the man,"
Donna mocked, recalling how her father smiled
And how she laughed those days on the divan.
And now that Edenic play stood reconciled
With something horrid, something charlatan.
She smirked her charge: "Since there was such foul bobbing
        'tween us—
Dad and me—has Bob designs on my male-child's anus?"

That night o'er dinner, she told her husband, "Touch
Seldom my Don. Ne'er bounce him on your knee.
He's not for nestling, specially near your crotch,
And not for fondling—Fondling!—familiarly.
A fatherly distance keep. If you so much
Not do what I demand, it's goodbye to me."
Bob knew new mothers tended toward the "all-possessive,"
So meekly agreed to be the father unaggressive.

"Is this the epic of Donna? Or is it Don's?"
I hear you asking. "Please speed up a little.
We are not—yet—a congregation of nuns
Who bide their time awaiting Glory's acquittal.
We've things to do. Remember that time runs,
Not crawls as a slug, down-weighed by its spittle."
Dire Reader, pardon. (But I should ne'er be so gauche as
You've been to me—and your simile's quite atrocious!)

Do you want speed? I'll show I can encapsule.
Don spent sev'n years beneath his mother's wings.
He had no playful mates, only the lap full
Of love she offered through her apron strings.
That is until that day he got a map full
Of the foreign. He was at his backyard swings
As pure and innocent as an Adamic cully,
When he heard voices, voices from a nearby gully

Beyond his yard, behind the fence whose gate
He'd never opened. . . . Laughing voices . . . He looked
Toward his house. Why wasn't his mother at
The window where she should be, yes, be? He crooked
A leg to heighten the swing's arc. . . . "Hale voices that
Laugh laughter unknown to me." He unhooked
The safety strap. . . . After a fall (or was it a jump?)
He flew across the fence, and found himself in a clump

Of bushes, hanging over the gully's edge.
They were three boys, two in their middle teens;
The other would have been about Don's age.
All three were wearing those ragged blue jeans
His mother forbad. Their shirts hung from a hedge,
And half-naked, half-hidden by the den's
Cool shade, they lulled. The blond one lay in weeds, thus darker
Seemed. When he laughed, to Don it was a devil's laughter.

The other older boy held a cigarette,
And after drawing on it, with a toss
Flipped it to the blond. His left hand's white
Fingers snared it. "Man, that's a good good–pass,"

He smiled. "And catch. You're quite an ath(e)lete;
Didn't miss a stroke." . . . "But why is the tall grass
Moving, jostling, there where the blond's right hand is hidden?"
Don wondered. "For though I stretch my body and widen

My eyes, what it's up to my mind can not
Make out." Deep cast were the shadows of the oak
Trees across the gully's weedy under-knot.
But the youngest boy's intense gaze bespoke
That there was more, more in the tall grass plot
Where toiled the right, than in the left hand's smoke.
"Youngun, you come on here, and touch what you do look on,"
The blond one fleered. His stopped right hand arose to beckon.

The other teen then giggled, "C'mon, kid."
He slapped the boy on the back, a playful shove.
With striving awe, Don watched the boy, who tried
To move his legs, but neither leg would move.
The boy's eyes showed he saw what the tall weeds hid
From Don. "If lovely won't come, I'll bring my love
To him." The blond—to Don now terrible as thunder—stood
Up. And at that point Don saw, and seeing Don understood.

The blond then took the young one's hand and drew
It slowly toward him. Now the other fellow's
Eyes fixed on what Don firsthand feared to view.
Instead, averting, Don's focussed on the shadows,
Where too sullied flesh took on a dream's hue:
"A shadowed hand does touch and now mouth follows,"
Don saw and said. And bolted—no mo' the coy-boy cully—
For home, his map o'erfilled, and now its shape, a gully.

Don heard her greeting: "Hon, been on the swing?
I couldn't watch. Was on the phone with that noise
Next door, ole Mrs. Rush. Sit down. I'll bring
You some milk and Or—Your new corduroys,
How'd that weed stain get there?" Not meant to sting
The words, snake-like, did. "Momma," the boy's
Words shot forth, "I love you. Only you. About the stain
I'm sorry. I promise it won't happen e'er again."

A mother's favorite child–sent word, "Sorry,"
Caused Donna to draw Don close. With a hug
Becoming tighter, she said, "Don't worry,
Pet. I've caught your every sneeze" (a tug
At his nose) "and scrubbed your hunky-dory"
(She goosed him) "and there's been many a plug
Of you-know-what would stick" (her hand tapped at his asshole)
"'Til Momma scrubbed away that stinking casserole.

. . . I love you true." And though those words sincerely
Were drawn, they were received as a hollow sound,
For Don knew that he'd used "I love you" merely
To turn aside his mother, not respond
Directly to her "staining" question. This dear lie—
Unbeknownst—became the breaking of a bond.
His mother's smile and kiss were "welcome home" to the sully
And stain that he himself had brought home from the gully.

Don put aside that black hole, set out to be
What his mother wished, and not just to please her,
Rather out of fear at what *he* might see
If he looked too deeply into that dark fissure,

Where dwelt a prisoner, like one medievally
Doomed and forgotten by his cruel sentencer:
Entombed yet free, for he could roam his cell and scrape
Against its walls, each chink holding the hope of escape.

Before I hear you cough, as quick as thunder
I'll join our hero when he was 25.
18 years will I pass by in a plunder
Since you like epics writ in overdrive.
Thank goodness, for I had begun to wonder
How I could bring that interval alive,
It being Duns-Scotus dull, a decorous formality,
As happens when th' *ur*-normal strains for normality.

A joyous day: Don (lately Ph.D.'ed)
Was to be wed. It's true he had not reached
The summit Donna had pre-scaled, but he'd
Neither fallen once nor publicly impeached
Her chosen family name with vile misdeed.
He'd passed the life which she had proudly preached,
Ne'er dozing through a sermon, no bucker of her schemes.
And now he was to marry: the girl of *her* dreams.

"Her pedigree's pure, all-Americana.
Her father's pockets deep and thickly lined
With gold more golden than *Ex.*'s gold manna,"
She had sold her bill of goods to Don. "A find
Not seldom found. And open. No arcana
About her. All outward, nothing hid behind,
Which men abominate, remembering Eden's serpentry.
And Botticelli beautiful. I vow she'll keep her pantry

As spotless as her soul. Her name is Anna!"
. . . "After one hour, nee Condor." Don let
A smile form on his lips, but no "Hosanna"
Tailed this recalling of that sermonette
His mother had intoned, "first of her *campagna*
To get me wed." He pushed aside the set
Of exams that had brought him to his college office
In tux, his "grooming" done before daybreak. "The coffee's

Bitter now," he sighed, yet took a fourth sup.
"We'll be happy. I have a mother's assurance,
None better." He drained the last lee from the cup.
"I'll wash it before I go. . . . Perdurance
Is all!" He headed to the men's room, up
One flight, each step exalting the allurance
Of the marriage bed and the certainty it'd work—
His penis—that night. "I'd better take a leak,"

He told himself. "The ceremony's long."
He put the cup unwashed down on the basin
With care, walked to a urinal, and hung
O'er it. He caught the shadow of his face in
The stained ceramic beyond his pee, the pang
Of recognition startling him. "I must hasten
Before my shadow o'ertakes me." To hurry the pace,
He shut his eyes. . . . Reopened, they saw a second face

Whose shadow had subsumed the urinal's
White-slurred surface, o'eriding Don's own.
"He must have stepped out from one of the stalls,"
Don thought. He glanced; behind him was a young man—

"As young as I once was"—in blue overalls
And a white T-shirt. The youth kneaded his groin,
Having taken the next urinal, and began to unbutton
The coppers of his fly. His lips were being bitten,

Don's third glimpse showed. "Already anxious at
Nineteen. What has the world come to, when its youth
Trembles before they're twenty?" And with that
Sad query, Don's eyes fell, consumed with ruth,
And further fell in flight, before they alit
On a cock so large Don let out a silent oath.
The youth then dug his balls out. In awe Don pondered, "How hard
A feat!" Then, looking down, he saw his own become now hard.

"And this my wedding day!" The young man's hand
Moved through the air— "An angel's? A devil's?
For both can fly, I've been made to understand,"
Don gasped inside. "To some, birds are evils;
To others, augurs. It's all as God's f'ordained."
While he with these theological upheavals
Wrestled, a hand landed on his cock and thereon lay.
"More the shock, *my* hand does fly. And this *my* wedding day!

The cock is near! The balls I hear!" (Don's groan)
"A wringing sound they make! My hand is drawn
Not on its own toward that I should disown.
No sinful *dies non*, it is the dawn,
The dawn of Don. (The bells I hear!) Alone
I palely loiter, while on the church's lawn
My bride awaits. 'Bells! Bells! Balls! No, Bells! Bells!' I say."
His hand did touch the young man's crotch. And this his wedding
          day!

The glisk did scald. Back jumped Don Jaunt and ran,
Both hands a-trying to cram inside his trousers
The serpent that had crawled from its pit. "De–man
Me not!" his cry. . . . The gayest of all carousers
At the wedding feast was Don. His publican
"I do" (*sotto*, "I didn't") rang. Of all espousers,
None happier came to bridal bed, cologned, washed up—
With but one cark: "Why did I leave behind the unwashed cup?"

Six more years on: Our Don has gotten tenure
And children two. ["Oh No!," you cry, "that /al/ /ild/
Once more obtrudes its sway, resettling in your
Ill epic. We thought we'd said a 'Farewell' (chilled)
To that o'er-rhymed scheme. Awaits another ten-year
Stint in Poetry's purgatory? 'Male-child'
Utter not again, we beg!"] And children two—both daughters.
('Tis you, not I, that muddy my poetic waters.)

The sex of her granddaughters did not displease
An older Donna. It's the mid '70's,
A time uneasy with gross prejudice,
Where, outdoing Eden, there were less uneven ties
Binding male and female. An eons-old disease
Was addressed by an era. Not heaven 'tis
Or heavenly yet, but a woman now could curse
As openly as a man and know the curse was hers.

"Damn!" hailed Donna. "I can revive my dreams
For Don." In that she had a neo-confidante,
A partner, who soaked up her previous schemes
And lent new ones, so Don would reach the want

Of which he was unaware. Donna spoke, "It seems
Since the Kennedys (for sure they still do haunt
Us, in spite of the abuse of bullets and dirty tricks
They've borne) life's apogee is found in power politics."

The words delighted Anna. She took the hint:
"Do you suggest Don don the hat political?"
Donna assured her, "Indeed 'twas what was meant."
They leaned their heads together; . . . and that political
Web they wove, last-stitched as President
Their Don (ne'er considering once he was all apolitical).
Their noggins drew back, one dream serpenting the other:
Anna as First Lady reigned; Donna, Primal Mother.

"We must not tell our Don of his horizon."
"Not a word," Anna concurred. And thus began
Their long crusade: Through season after season
At teas they poured, and charities also ran.
In tandem Don arose, quick deemed the Arisen
Man of Academia, soon to be a Dean.
Dragged here, dragged there, Don's fear in all these withals:
Of seeing/being seen by the youth in overalls.

The university conquered, these two ladies
Then set their sights on the municipal.
"'It's here a JFK's unmade or made' is
My first *donnee*," spoke Donna. "The political
Is a tough and rumpled game, and well-played is
Hard-balled. Can Don—our Don—take the ridicule
And all exposure it is fraught with. Seldom womenless,
I think his past is pure, is matchless, is—uh—sinless."

She paused. "But that 'seldom' bothers me." "And me too,"
Chirped Anna. Ere they joined the race for mayor,
They knew they had to search Don's soul's soul. "We two
Must learn if once he inhaled a 'weed,' say, or
Jaywalked—and there were Witnesses. We must see to
All those things, of which flesh is th' inheritor—
Before the opposition, who'll try to stain and sully
Our Don, seeking each toilet trace and trashed gully

Of his being! Game?!" Donna's voice reached a shriek.
"Yea! Verily Yea!" Anna's words, like a *heil*
Greeting a Hitler, burst forth. "Where to peek,
But tell me! Pry, but show me! Nothing I'll
Not do!" . . . "Set on him in your bed. There, seek,
Where men are vulnerable most to a woman's wile."
Exhausted both fell back, proud arms across their bellies:
"To get a Solon," thought each, "we must be Machiavellis."

That night ensued: In her blackest negligee,
And most alluring perfume, Anna crawled
Under the comforter and made her way
Across the bed to the side where Don was sprawled,
Most sleeping. "I love you. What more can I say?"
Her lips against his ear, her voice enthralled.
Both panicked Don. He thought, "My thing's funereal.
To get it up, I'll have to dream of the urinal."

(It was through such extreme hallucination
That Anna Donna/Donna Anna, his daughters,
Had been conceived—both born in desperation,
More fathered by the copper-buttoned halters

Of a pair of overalls.) A loud suspiration
As snore—which worked sometimes—and gibberish mutters
He let out. She cooed again, "On my finger a trust-band,
My greatest treasure, I wear. I love thee, dear husband!"

Her hand had not slid downward from his chest.
"Perhaps just wants to talk," Don hoped, Don prayed.
"I trust thee, and desire to have thy trust.
Hold nothing back from me—alackadayed—
As nothing from thee I bar." A giant thrust
Put her heart against his heart. Her tongue stayed
Mute a moment. "No wit how dark, reveal your innermost
Sin to thy trusty wife, knowing we're the sinner most

When we self-rely. Denied, I can't forgive.
Thus doubly denied: unheard sin, unspoke' pardon.
Though mother of thy children, know that I live
Only for thee!" "So long," agonized Don, "a guard on
The gully, the toilet I've kept. My soul does strive
To be released. . . . A sign I—Is that a hard-on
I have? . . . I have my sign! And not brought by the urinal!
I will confess, be wifely shrived of my sin original."

'Tis true her words had made his penis stir
And stiffen. Molten steel ran through that gland.
"My dearest Anna, there is one thing," and her
Heart seemed to skip a pound. "Or two—both unplanned,
Thus aboriginal—dalliances mere.
Hear and forgive. I lusted—" "I understand,"
She yelped with glee, "'—in your heart.' No more than Jimmy Carter.
An unwitnessed sin!" "No, darling, I lusted with my—" "Stand!

You Abha go, fly Abha. Stand! Go!" Don's eyes
Flamed open. His shoulders were being shaken.
"Plane, now." With such poor-Englished entreaties,
A Saudia agent sought to awaken
Don. "Miss plane, you." Don grabbed for his valise:
"No time, the toilet. I've got to get a shake-on,
Or I'll be stranded." (And I until a later vellum
Strand whether wife forgave or raged—*Pax Anna* or
    Anna Bellum—

This breaching being that prerogative
Of every epicist from Homer to Faulkner.
I hear you cry, "Get on with your [expletive
Deleted] plot!" To which I howl: I mock ne'er
My readers, to whom I merely wish to give
The savory suspense one gets in a walk near
A cliff. I wouldn't have left our dear Don's "lust" a-dangling
If I'd known it would bring on your petty wrangling.

I. e., who would not have preferred the *Iliad*
Minus the bickering of those gods and goddesses?)
I return: During this caesura, willy-nilly-ed,
Our hero reached Abha, his odyssey's
End. He was met by a daffy-down-dilly-ed
Egyptian, who said, "Me, I, Abdulhadi. See
Me bags you. Me get, go." Taken to an empty dorm, a
Downcast Don stared from a pane at the *terra non firma*

He'd struck upon: "No trees, no grass, no breath
Of air not clogged with dust. Trash everywhere.
All cinder-block buildings, their whitewash's swath
Now turned gray as gangrene. The witches' lair

In *Macbeth* had less stench to do battle with,"
Don moped. "Anna, are you happy that I bear
This cross? And, Mother, are you? Did my two dalliances
Merit this?" Down he fell, o'ercome by life's cruel phalanxes.

As I usually do, I'll use this time while Jaunt's
Asleep for a (single-stanzaed) exposition
On Abha, going beyond Don's drab complaints
About its air and smell. Its elevation,
C. 7000 feet; 80,000 inhabitants
Or so, a portion of whom needed education
In English. (Enter Don.) To Abha he's come to toil:
Poor Abha, the only spot in Arabia minus oil.

. . . Don thought he heard a knock. "It's Harvey Skewer
Here!" The door was opening at a corkscrew
Pace. A quite tall man came in. "God, what a sewer,
A Bette Davis dump of a place! Howchedo?"
He offered his hand. "Abdulhadi said two or
Three more'll be coming. For now, only you
And I." He sat down on the bed by Don's right leg. "You're
Don Jaunt. And I'm?"—he paused, testing Don—"I'm Harvey
          Skewer!"

"Hello," the hearing of his own name made Don speak.
"I need a coffee, and—Phew!—you need a shower,"
Skewer hurried in. "Flew straight-through? Now you reek.
Ah, I always try to stop o'er, if't's in my power.
This time in Athens. Two nights. Have some Greek
Friends." It was then Don noticed he had a flower
In his right hand. He offered it to Don, "A rose,
A Hellene gave me, 'fast faded.' Heaven only knows

When I'll get another! Not many flower beds
In Abha, eh?" Don took it instinctively.
"Up now! You've slept enough. 'Twas like the dead's
Sleep, the way you were snoring this morning when I
Peeked in. Bath, coffee, and then put our heads
Together, to see how we can 'make this misery
Merrier'—a motto of mine." "I've slept in my clothes,"
Don saw and said. He got up, still clutching the rose.

. . . "'Cleanliness is next to'—say it's in my genes,
So strongly I hold it—'Godliness,'" Don heard
As he left the bathroom. (He self-mused, "By jeans
Of blue and overalls, I'm here.") "It's absurd
How dirty the Arabs keep themselves. Hygiene's
Laws are unknown to them. In Libya the first word
From my mouth to students was 'Bathe. Bathe before you come
To my class.' Don saw that Harvey had *ad libitum*

Opened his suitcase, taken a shirt, a pair
Of pants, etc. from it, and was trying to smooth
Out some wrinkles. "As soon as one came through the door
Of my apartment, I'd bundled that unkept youth
(Protesting) to the toilet. 'Not before
You're clean can you come call on me,' my mouth
Bespoke. 'Clean from yah cranium down past yah tibia'
I ordered. (D'ji mention I taught five years in Libya?)"

Skewer paused, as if in pleasant reverie.
"And still be there if a friend had not called,
'Harvey, the vicious Libyan constabulary
Have raided your flat, just sacked it, and hauled

Off all sorts of things. I'd be leery
About coming back.' In a flash, I recalled
The Saudis were always in need of American
English Professors. It's true: I was hired via the phone.

That was two weeks ago. And you?" The towel
Folded, Don said, "Mine also was sorta easy:
Just a two–minute interview in Houston. 'You'll
Be able to leave right away,' said a grog-dizzy
Ancient—" "The Saudi's employment jewel,
Mrs. Dowhan," Harvey chuckled. "Hires in a breeze. I
Think it's time for *cafe au lait* and maybe a
Sambusa sweet." He paused. "Jaunt, welcome to Arabia!"

Since Skewer will be our Sancho (mayhap Quixote),
I think it fit to take a stanza out
And list his person's particulars; no bloaty
Account, I assure you: In age about
10 over Don's; dark hair ("a toupee?"); dirty
Brown eyes; a throaty voice which seemed to shout
E'en when it whispered; a bowled belly, and the panache
Of a peacock, or a 1947 coupe Nash.

In three days—through Harvey's revving—they had
A car, a villa of two flats, and their offices
At the College. The pace—with its myriad
Of maneuvers—giddied Don, but every crisis
Harv laughed at, laughed off, as a limp charade.
It was what he hinted, o'er coffee or ices
In the tearoom of Abha's expatriate (and only decent)
Hotel, that most rattled Don. The innuendoes he sent

Were always the same, th' unsubtle sexual:
E. g. "That E–gypt has donned an undersized
Gallibiya [robe] to highlight how more than full
His crotch is. He-he." "A Saudi who's exercised,
Irons his pump each night, I wager." "Quite a pull
To his Jordanian tug, eh Jaunt?" The comments terrorized
Don. It was as if they were meant to bring a confession
From his lips. "Oh no! 'I been there before.' Repression

Is all!" he vowed. "Let Skewer flaunt his want.
I'll not bite or be bitten. I've hit near bottom
(Arabia), can I sink to a lower haunt?
Siberia? Mauritania? . . . I've got 'im
As a villa mate, but with a staunch 'I don't'
I'll meet his every 'Do you?' No Sodom
Will I play to his born-again, worn-awry Gomorrah?
I won't be boxed in, not when the box is a Pandora."

The fourth night came: On what passed as a divan
In Arabia (6' x 4' rectangular
Sponge cushions, brightly colored), they sat, the span
Of a body's length separating. "Astir
I was tonight, I guess you saw," Harvey began,
Each airy word becoming solider
(Or so it seemed to Don, who squirmed). They had just come
From the hotel. "Thank God for poverty!" A hum

Followed the exclamation. Don recalled
What had happened: Not ten-minutes seated,
Harvey had stood up, given a nod bolder than bold
To the Somalian-clad youth, whose smile had greeted

Them as they had entered the tearoom. Appalled,
Don had watched as Skewer's leer had become "fetid,
. . . Beyond lurid," the very words of Don's o'erridden
Mind. The young man's eyes had tailed Harvey as he'd stridden

Past him, bound for the Bahaira's downstairs toilet.
Not allowing even half a minute to interpose,
The Somalian had sprung up, following. "I'll let
Myself no further be involved. Does Harv suppose
I wish to sully my life—again—soil-spoil it?"
For ten minutes Don had cursed, then resolved, "I'll arise
And ex—" "Delightful boy! 'I, little money! I, no job!'
He pled. So I gave him ten, and he gave me blow job,"

The words had been soft whispered in Don's ear,
Come from a leaned-o'er shadow. Skewer had
Reseated himself, sipped from his cup, "A dear
He was! And my coffee's not gotten cold.
'Tempus non fugit,' I say, when you're
Having fun." He had glanced toward Don. "Get ahold
Of yourself, old chum! How your hands shake! Get a handle,
I resay! Spilling your coffee in a hotel: *Quel scandal!*"

. . . "Yes, thank God for poverty!" ("Oh me! Oh my!"
Don moped to himself.) "But by the Glorious God o' me,
I don't like toilet trade. Too mundane! I
Prefer a more bizarre reeling o' my rod." ("Oh me!
Oh my!") "A bus, a shaft, etc. One night in Tripoli
I took all o' an embassy guard's big wad—" ("Oh me!
Oh my!") "—in his wee sentry cubicle, a prod o' me
I'll ne'er forget. . . . I yearn to be the Saint of Sodomy—"

("Oh me! Oh my!") "—and have my own canonical
Day; 'til that time—but enough of H. Skewer.
Your turn to speak, Jaunt." Don saw a satanical
Glint come to Harv's eyes; no promise to be true or
Trusty was in them. He recalled the manacle
Of innocence which Anna had used as the sly lure
To bind him. "None of her angel-laced chicanery
Do I see in Harvey's visage, simply a 'for-the-deviltry'

Grin." Don came round slowly: "A face I can trust
Because it says it cannot be trusted." Soon,
Don's words were hymning like to a skylark's burst
Of melody before heaven's gate. But none
Need I intone, Dire Reader. For they were thrust
Down your throat as far back as Stanza Ten.
"Up to his 'lusted with my—'" do I hear you grumble?
So it's there I'll take up, Your Epicist Most Humble.

Don: "'. . . with my hand.' Nowise did she withdraw,
And clutched me still, aye, even as my tongue
Exposed the gully, dark, where first I saw
The map that was to be myself. And tighter clung
As the urinal first in part, then over all,
Upswooped me. I finished; still her body wrung
My body, thrimbling it with a Heaven-based sympathy.
'Now thou shalt sleep,' she said, . . . and gave me kisses three.

. . . 'Congratulations, son, you've upped your dad
In this. I never once could knock my Donna off
Her feet.' I had awakened and found a bed
Empty. The whole house empty. 'Ah, my love,

Knowing my last night's strain,' I'd thought and said,
'Has early left with the girls, afraid a cough
Might wreck my morning.' It was then I saw the smear
Of lipsticked words across the frig: 'Queer, Queer, Queer, Queer.'

'Just a bruise on her head, but shattered that kitchen
Table, her fall.' Dad's voice, two miles away,
Seemed closer than it'd ever been. 'Which in
A way completes the circle. Son, that day
When she told me about the change, that switch in
Your name, I said she'd que—uh—make you gay.
(I've read your kind prefer—more correct politically—
To be called that.) She's at the hospital; A. D.,

D. A., and Anna are sitting with her. She came
To once and heard the chant the girls can't stop
Singing, "Daddy's a que—gay!" Screamed the blame
On me, tried to climb from the bed. "I'll lop
Off his cock and balls. (A knife! A knife! My queendom
For a knife!) No use to him—the flippity-flop!"
I left as they were putting on a stronger straightjacket;
Couldn't stomach anymore, D.A./ A.D.'s singsong racket.

Some fatherly advice. If I were you, son,
I'd get out of Macon . . . Georgia . . . the U.S.A.
You got no job—oh, I thought you knew, son,
The Dean called "Fired" in earlier. And that day
Will come when they'll let her out. No new sun
Will she wait for. Better get as far away
As you can, for she's a Medea, will track you down.
Bye, my Don.' For fully five minutes I clutched the phone,

Refusing to admit the line was dead."
No sooner had Don stopped than Harvey's, "Your
Peccavi: A cock-touched hand—all you did!
(The peeping-Tomism doesn't rate a 'mere.')
And that's made you feel solidly sullied.
That's the entire, the circular, . . . for sure."
Don nodded. "My solemn judgment, Jaunt, is that you're
99 and 44/100% pure.

. . . I'll have to see what I can do 'bout—uh—that."
And Skewer fell into a fit of laughter.
He rolled on the carpet like an acrobat
From the *commedia dell'arte*. "It's after
Midnight, Harvey, hush! Hush! Our neighbors, at
Their sleep, will hear. Hush!" Harv: "To every rafter
In Georgia let it ring! 'The bells! The bells! The balls!'"
Soon, to his shock, Don joined in, chimed in, "And toilet stalls!"

"None truer than Harvey Skewer!"—another
Of his mottoes, always said with all the fervor
Of that age-old more popular adage, "My oath [or
Word]'s my bond"—was vouched the next night. "Your server"—
He stood before Don's door—"No Martin Luther,
The never-kneed, I bow." Harv bowed. This swerve or
"Genuflection" (Don's word) exposed—in all his grand allure—
A dashing Turk. "He's yours. Eh, 'None truer than Harvey
          Skewer'?"

That night Don's scarce-soiled hand, his virgin mouth,
Edenic asshole—all had their frock and flower *de-*'ed.
The Ottoman's Grand Scimitar slashed south,
Plunged north. Like Shelley, a woeful, all-full Don pled—

But no words could stop the Turk in his wrath—
"I fall upon the thorn of life! I bleed!"
And more, "I am 'destroyed,' 'preserved' through every jerk
And thrust of my 'seed-spreading' and 'uprooting' Turk."

In a rush, I'll hustle to the second night
And Don's second lover; this one our Don
Himself had picked up, a—What scream of plight
Is that? Is it the dawn of Oblivion?
Judgment's Blast? Bleating Titans in their flight
From Zeus? What Juggernautian carrying on!
Oh me! Oh my! I tremble! "And well you should, dull
Epicist. There is a point where cock becomes all bull.

Your readers speak: We'd prefer a Gabriel,
Tartarus interment, or to be overlaid
Aft' throwing ourselves beneath a Vishnu wheel
To what you've planned, a night-by-night parade
Of Jaunt's conquests. Is that what you so call
'The epical'? And like a Scheherazade
Wilt drag it out and out to 1001?
We'll read no more unless you put your signature upon

The dotted line of this contract: 'I attest
(1) my epic has "terminus," (2) I'll roll
Infinity into one—two, at th' uttermost
(Meaning not just Don's nights, but the whole
Of Skewer's also), and (3) I'll do my best
To confine myself to the heroic—the soul
Of the Homeric, etc. epic—getting as close to
That grand mark as I can (e.g., no Ariosto).'

Sign here or we depart." It is a messy
Milieu—O Calliope, join in my weeping!—
When Art has as its Helmsman one whose *esse*
Is bent on scuttling—through Bligh-like o'er-peeping
Each shoulder—our Stately Craft in its gest. (I
Mourn, ye bow-maid, reduced to demirepping!)
O readers, ken not such ogling may pull apart and warp
The woods of each Artist's Argonaut? From thorp

To metropolis, aye, Art will be "bound
In shallows," there to thrash. This known, I see change
A-creeping into your eyes. The bold demand
Of your contract—enforcing on me, "Change
Your epic's style or we'll seek a new epic land"—
Now you wish to withdraw; instead beg, "No wee change
Make in your epyllion. We love Grand Literature!"
It's so! . . . Is't so? . . . "Sir, be brief! Your signature!"

. . . I've signed it. Blah! Now are you satisfied?
. . . "To two," you say. "At uppermost!" How to choose
From all the jewels in my crowning epic? I'd
Better put aside that one. Does abuse
Condition (3), I fear: Don's been cow-tied,
Across his kitchen table, while three perfuse
Across his body's surface oil-drenched, gooey *homous*
(Bean-paste). No, that tale of barbecue might break my promise.

And this one: Harvey is being set upon
By six dung-lusty Yemenis, and each
In panic seeks a hole to make his own,
Several finding that they must share a breach

With brother, or get none. Harvey's long moan
(Ten-stanzaed) unspirits (2) in its overreach:
He (like an Empress Theodora) surveyed his Yemen three
+ three and prayed, "Great God, why so few points of entry

Ye've graced our mortal bodies with? Divine
Cruelty in its unusefulness!" . . . *Eureka!*
I've lit on one which steps not o'er the line
Of your conditions. I'm sure it's what you seek, a
Tale sublime, all-*gravitatus*. In fine,
It out-chivalries the most chivalric. Aye,
Of all my *Saint*, 'twill be the passage sage anthologists
Will choose to "purple" (but turn green other chronologists—

He-he!) You think it well-knit when Theseus
Twined a Minotaur, or Jason *et al.*
Fleeced Colchis? Or grand when Cerberus
Was tied by Herakles (the first leash-law
Enforcer)? Or droll when Tantalus
Dared stuff the Gods with his boiled son? Your recall
Of these (and such-like) mythic feats will seem unreal
After you have heard of Harv's 69-hour ordeal.

"None bluer than Harvey Skewer!"—Tacked on an "Alas!"—
Was our Don's suspiration in its *in toto*.
(Four months have duly lapsed; I've had to pass
O'er some 666 lovers, given the "Go to
Goal" ultimatum you set.) "Sans cock, sans ass,
For two long weeks. Is my best friend's new motto,
'Make merriment more miserable?' What does he grapple
With, whose face holds all the glee of a chopped-down Maypole?"

'Tis true, for eight nights Harv had sadly opened
The front door of their villa and spoken *Mah fee*
(There isn't), driving out all of the hope and
Expectant joy from each youth's face. Not even a coffee
Offered, even to those well-hung who would grope and
Squeegee their crotch. In Arabic, some pled, "No fee,
Mister Harv, I ask. Please, I sit awhile on your divan?
No money." Each received the wan reply, *"Ana taban,"*

A phrase most difficult to wend from Arabic
Into English. Its literal translation,
"I am tired," conveys none of the plethoric
Overflow of the phrase's connotation,
Which can range from "I'm sleepy," to "I'm sick
With a cold, etc." or to a broad damnation
Of life and living. E. g., a broken fingernail
Or a self-imposed descent into the Dantest hell

Can invoke an *"ana taban."* Don had at first
Not asked, "What's *taban*?"— much less "Which one is it?"
Harv's "Cover my classes, will you?" was not "the worst
A friend from another friend could elicit,"
Don had thought 14 days ago. "Not fate accursed,
Given all he's done for me. Probably had a visit,
From some Moroccan late last night and waylays his male
With Juliet's plea: '. . . Not the lark . . . It was the nightingale.'"

Returned that dusk, Don asked not, but with a bow,
Stated through the crack in Harv's door, "I bet
I know which part of you is oh-so *taban* now."
The joke had fallen flat; all he could get

From Harvey was "I'll soon be ok." His brow
(All Don had seen) was—more the shock—whitely wet.
"I'll fetch a—" had been parried by the door's being shut.
These words beyond: "Handle the traffic, the general glut."

Don had done so, covering Harv's lovers as well
As his classes. He had accepted that all mortals,
H. Skewer no longer excluded, fall within the pale
Of Depression's shadow. "He's good at hurdles,
And more of concern to me, his fare–thee–well:
How will I handle the double flow at my portal's
Doorway? He-he." Fifth day: Don was as much at wit's end
As Harvey's crew; he missed, as much as the crew, his true friend.

"Love is by silence checked: sex must be noised."
(Don's mope) "Where is its joy when each blow-by-blow
Has no grinner, ear-to-ear (both equipoised),
In whom to confide? . . . I'll force him up! I'll go
No more when his doorbell's rung." He had rejoiced
That night when on the 20th chime Harvey's slow
Footfalls attested he budged. And then *that* word so wan,
Forcing Don to plumb the depths of Harvey's *taban*.

Seven days of *agon*; then Don summ'ned the courage
To confront his friend with what he had concluded.
Don banged; Harv oped; Don's whine, "It does occur; age
Brings it on. There's no shame! Not to be brooded
Upon, that things below no longer bestir; age
Is the culprit. . . . You've missed what I've alluded
To, your puzzled face shows. So the pseudonym, potent,
I'll put aside and bluntly speak: 'You've become all impotent!'"

Backward fell Harvey. Using the widening crack,
Don intruded into his pale friend's apartment.
Harv mounted his bed as if it were a rack,
Sighed and said, "I know what your tongue and heart meant:
But I have fallen *not* into that *cul de sac*
All gays dread. Nothing wrong with that department
Of mine. See." Harv loosed the drawstrings of his pajamas.
They dropped. The tool Don saw made him exclaim, "Holy Mamas!"

"It is my soul that's shrunk. Or the realization
That it has," Harv 'wailed, "not reached greatness' due."
'Tis true I had half Tripoli's male population
Between 18 and 27, but who
Didn't, . . . who can't? If numbers are elevation
To an Olympian height, its thereinto,
Consider Athens: The hordes I had, counting boy by boy,
Exceeds the Greeks who fell beneath the walls of Troy."

Harv buried his face, but erstwhile removed a hand.
"All numbers, vain numbers, merely one affair
Piled on another, a Babel built on sand,
Mocking me as . . . 'The Greatest of Gays.' Not there,
One epic feat saying to our future band,
'Look on my work, ye Gaiety, and despair!'
What have I truly done—and isn't it so odd o' me—
To think I deserve to be dubbed, 'The Saint of Sodomy'?"

An Ajaxian heft came from his bowl-like belly.
Don crept close, sat on the bed so that a sector
Of his left buttock touched Harvey's knee. "The melee
Of Myrmidons hath never seen a more perfect or

Perfected warrior than thou, my friend. Really,
Thou'st put to heel Achilles, outstripped Hector!"
"But," Harv whined, "is mine the ass that launched a thousand
        ships?
Are my cock and balls on each heroic poet's lips?

Nay! Nay! I hear the music of the hautboys;
My greatness-to-be (like Antony's) now leaves me."
Dire-struck, Don struck a blow on Harv's hams, "No boys
Deserve to die, these unplumbed. How it grieves me,
Harv, to see your 'giving up.' Rather sing, 'O boys!
I'll con a trick to o'ercome these glooms that seize me.
Your Harvey Skewer will return more true than truer,
Affirming'—as I affirm— 'None truer than Harvey Skewer!'"

Having caught the twinkle of Harv's abashed glance
That he wanted, Don exited and waited.
A span of two days: Harv had assumed the stance
Of a steely warrior; 'twas a Giant that greeted
Don Jaunt. "My friend, I'll need your assistance
When comes the time," he hobnobbed. The unabated
Nod a King expects Don gave. "Now I into the wilds
Near Abha go." His mien: godly; his eyes: a childe's.

A month and ten days whisk by: At 3 a.m.
The knock came. "I've found *him*; he—and I—must rest
Two days (for epic feats all turn to gross mayhem
When rushed). Suffice to say the grandest gest
E'er dreamed by gays is at hand (the slight per diem
I'm gifting him not sullying a whit the contest).
I've learned 'tis 'on time' not 'o'er time' greatness doth show
(For why else is the *Odyssey* so ranked a step below

The *Iliad*?). In epics the only
True number is 1 on 1, not adventures
So outstretched that bones o'erweighing a ton lie
About the battlefield: Achilles/Hector's,
Christ/Satan's, Beowulf/Grendal's ma's so–lonely
Duels. Ah, 'The hero enters,' not 're-enters.'
And 'tis with me: I would roll love, aye its barrel-and-stock,
Into this: How long can I keep it locked up an ass, my cock?"

Back in his bed, Don knew the venture his friend
Had been embarked upon these past long forty
Days: To find the perfect asshole was his end.
"Not deep-set," reasoned Don anally. "A shorty
Can enter it easily—and Harv's sword's a Godsend—
But deep, can take all—point, foible and forte,
Up to the hilt—never releasing, once in its cincture's
Grasp. Oh yes, an ass full-mighty in its sphincters!"

Awhile on, Don a wager made with himself.
"I've held mine up a Palestinian's ass
For 34 minutes, and I'm in truth a dim self,
A shadow, compared to Harv. He'll o'erpass
My record by ten, I bet. Once in the swim, self
And soul fine-tuned, Harv—Paterfamilias
Of Gays—will draw upon all of his untapped powers
And not withdraw his cock for seven—nay, eight—hours."

. . . "A wee bit fidgety—for a hero should strut—"
Don self-carped, as he, the designated recorder,
Entered Harv's bedroom, the edgily shut
Door not going unnoticed. "A portent of disorder,"

He thought. "This is Saad," Harv said. An up-turned butt,
All of the man he could see, squiggled "a word or
So of acknowledgment" (Don's *idee*). "Ready for your cock watch,
Jaunt?" Harvey tittered. "Oh good, you didn't forget the stopwatch."

Harv climbed atop. "I'm in!" with exaltation
He cried, but not until the confirming "You're in!"
From Don was the button pushed. At his fixed station
He had enchaired himself, there to abjure, in
All the God-knows-how-long cohabitation,
That Harv's not once slipped out. "I'll be cocksure in
My recording," Don vowed. "With sentried head—though it may
        pain us—
Fixed 'twixt four legs, I'll nae take eye from cock or anus."

As lazily as a Serengeti lion
Arouses on a dew-sotted summer's morn,
Disturbed not one wit by the tsetse fly on
His still-asleep left ear, and keeps still-born
Even a twitch of his tail, as disdainful scion
To gross awakening, held in highborn scorn,
So slowly came Harv's second thrust, scarce climacteric,
Inside. [Dear Reader, note the simile Homeric!

How over-well I meet Condition (3)!]
"The slug-like pace attests to his marathon
Mindset," Don chortled, but soon snipped off his glee,
For third and fourth and fifth came on/were gone
Inside a second. Such pile-driving industry
Ensued that Don in panic threw his hands upon
Harv's hips. He tugged until the fiery pounding was banked.
"Sorry," Harv sighed, "but 'tis the sweetest meat e'er butcher
        shanked.

I'll not lose my head again." And since none truer
Than Harvey Skewer in his word, Don relaxed
And reassumed his seated post. Nothing askew or
Untoward occurred the next four hours. . . . Transfixed,
Don almost did not hear the pleading, "You're
Ok, Mister Harvey? . . . I not." Harv's vexed
Reply o'erran the simple Arabic Don understood,
As did Saad's answer. Harv cursed. Then the two—to Don's
          wonder!—stood

Up, aft' much sclaffing, sliding 'cross the sheet.
"He's got to piss. The anti-diuretic
Pills," Harv mumbled, as in tandem to the toilet
They shuffled, "of course, I took. Saad's physic:
Two days of enemas and an indiscreet
Dose of Imodium." Keeping check that Harv's prick
Stayed in, a crouched-o'er Don was spoken down to. "You're
          seeing
The point, aren't you, Jaunt? I had to stop his shitting, my peeing."

"A prowessed Ajax, and the wily mental
Powers of a sage Ulysses," Don marveled.
"You've nothing left to the lapsing accidental,
To occult luck, or faulted fate, star-veiled."
Harv smirked, "I rated one-per-one excremental
Hole would suffice as testament of a far-vailed
Noblesse oblige, a hero's requisite, quite secure in
My calcula—Be careful, Saad, you're splashing urine

All o'er the rim of the toilet bowl." Don, who
Had stuck his head between their legs to confirm

The lock, because of his up-close underview
Received some ricocheting sprinkles. With a squirm
He freed himself from this 2-personed *prie-dieu*,
Swearing it tasted "of vinegar and sperm."
"You too near got to the root of the root of all evil,"
Harv mocked, "and now are privy of the Paradise Primeval."

As they wend their way from toilet back to bed,
I'm sure you want a portrait drawn of Saad.
I'll use the one Don framed, as not ill-said:
"A *Bedu* [Bedouin] youth; his age—a slipshod
Guess—19 to 28; bedspread
Thin, both in bone and flesh; a country clod,
He'd be called in Georgia; almost ugly; no prod o' me"
Don shuddered, "he'd get. That is the Saad I saw, the Saad o' me."

The ninth hour came ("And I have lost my wager,"
Don gaped, "and happily has it been lost!"):
Harv spoke, "A man's stomach is his best gauger;
I hear Saad's rumble; 'tis time for tea and toast."
They slowly moved, careful not to disengage or
Let Harvey's cock spurt out. "We'll play the host,"
He continued, and as a one-backed beast with double
Waddle they reached the kitchen, evincing less trouble

In their short steps than Don who like a frog
Hopped at their sides, his eyes on the *coitus*
Ne'er flinching. While Harv poured, a monologue
Spilled out: "...I'll... toast... Saad... tea... Meager... effete
     ... us—"
A half-hearing Don jumped in, "The epilogue

Is near, my friend? When have you goaled the quietus
Of your gest?" Harv's face showed hurt: "I've set sights on no
          'gimme,'"
He snarled. "Why my cock's not yet gone from hard to semi–!"

. . . "Can someone cover my classes, also Harv's?
. . . Oh yes, a bug [Don had withheld the -*gery*]
We're both down with." The Saudi Dean's "Yah starves,
Yah knows, ze fevry . . ." dragged on in its *de jure*
Crude-Englished *adviso*. Don surveyed his nerves,
The phone put down: "They are a whirling flurry.
The 52nd hour's come and gone. They've slept—
I haven't. And even in his sleep ole Harv has kept

His cock not only in, but often moving.
I've heard of a sleepwalker, but a sleepfucker!"
Don stumbled back to his mark. An approving
Glint from Harv's eyes met him. "Eh Jaunt, a deep fucker
Am I? Invigorates. I could keep shoving
Until the cows come home. Ever a sheep fuck or
Fondle back in Georgia, Jaunt? And what about my Berber
[Sic] Saad?" Harvey splathered on. "A Houri jewel, none superber!"

. . . An exclamation: "The time, Jaunt, the time?"
By then Don was seeing twin cocks in twin asses.
"69 and a quarter," Don slurred. "I'm
Up for more, but fear my reach o'erpasses
Saad's grasp. His hole has gone from grime to slime,
And though he doesn't complain, complaining gases
Arise from it. A Hillary must to his Sherpa
Condescend. 'Tis time to cry, 'Hold, enough,' to extirp a

Root that does not desire to be uprooted,
But strives to climb down to the lowest reaches
Until earth's molten center is saluted
And embraced." He sighed, "The breach of all breaches,
No mo' I'll into, yet with an undisputed
Vigor will close my epic quest. 'Cum,' not speech, is
Called for." His voice exultant grew. "Yea, with an inhuman
Burst I'll fountain Saad's Arcady asshole with my semen!"

Don—who had squired his Harv through every moment,
Had massaged his limbs (and Saad's), both bathed with sponge,
Cleaned up the bed once known what Harv's "uh-oh" meant
(A fart had come out juicy), even made a lunge
To catch young Saad whose podical bestowment
Would have slid out when he slipped, a downward plunge
Which would have midway ended the test—felt a phoenix
Quandary: "What if in entering Glory's fire he nicks

Not Time, but overtaxes his Great Heart,
Burns himself up and arises not from the ashes?"
(The fears of every hero's counterpart
From Patrocles to Bardolph's fretful flashes
About his Falstaff, as if once at the start
A Hamlet has an easy exit, a cache's
Corner to hide from his fate.) Don knew 'twas true for
His Harvey, and "how senseless is my prolonged 'rue-for.'"

"As ominous unseen ionic particles
Dart through the air, and through their otic sense
Are picked up by prescient animals, oracles
Hence of the coming earthquake's turbulence,

So a trembling aura suffused the bed, the articles
About it, indeed the room's walls," a tense
Don noted, "'though the bed's two bodies have so limber
Become it is hard to separate member from member.

1 on 1 has become 1." His admiration
Blazed forth. "In love's country, neither the conquered
Nor the conqueror is!" . . . With soft, slow undulation
As that which greets the craft once unanchored,
Saad's ass rose and fell. With sure-keeled navigation
Harv's cock ingathered silent strength. . . . No clank heard
Nor cacophony from their love-making, all Spherical
Music (to close this stanza, with its metaphorical

Mix of land, sea and air; fire understood.)
. . . The motionless maelstrom broke at the Still Point:
Richter–reeled, caught in the backdraft of his loosed manhood,
Harv was hurled—smashed 'gainst a wall! . . . He grogged,
          "Aye, we'll point,
We gays, to this grave climax—and well we should—
When love took wings and flew. . . . A codicil point,
You might think it, Jaunt; I don't: How's my Saad? Did he survive?
My vision's fuzzy—and well it should be; I'll not forgive

Myself if he's succumbed." Don looked and saw
And said: "The fireball of your 'cum' has blasted
The youth through sheet/mattress/springs in its heave-ho.
The bed's collapsed o'er him. Has he outlasted
His undertowing ordeal, I do not know.
I—and the hereafter world—will be flabbergasted
If so he has." Harv's body struck the wreck at roquet
Pace. Hands dug . . . until the words, "Mister Harv, I do ok?"

In questioning quaint Arabic issued forth
From the bed's disheveled stuffing, but no bit
Disturbed was the youth who stepped out. Ne'er earth
More welcomed the sun's rays, exquisite,
Than Harv his Saad. They cooed, consumed with mirth . . . .
"He said he has an ocean of 'cum' to excrete,"
Harv commented, after the youth with much pardoning
Had left for the toilet. "As for me, I'm artery-hardening

To know if I hit my mark. The time, old man?"
"69:22" was Don's quick reply.
"And so did I symbolically f'ordain:
Two numbers sacred to gays." A smile all-wry
Came 'cross Harv's visage. "No need to explain
The '69.' The second, by-and-by,
Will come to you." Don mused, self-offering signaled plan on plan.
Harv snorted. "Dullard, 2,2: They bugger, kneeling man on man."

Let three days pass: Saad, graced with an enlarged bonus
To augment his 20-*riyal*-an-hour pay,
Had left (all smiles), "with a much enlarged anus
And piles aplenty," Don grinned. Sleep's sway,
"Well-deserved," had held Harvey. "His epic onus
Lifted, I'll find him all—" Instead a lackaday
Harv greeted him: "Woe's me! I weep! After all my penis's
Ordeal, 'twill never be set down . . . in the book of the Guinnesses.

A fucking record ne'er to be recorded.
Alas!" "Great friend!" With stammering essays,
Don vowed, "I'll epi—" But his words were swarded
By a glimmering impishness in Harvey's gaze,

"Not for Guinness glory, I—on my word—did
It, but in the sight of God, and for all gays.
A feat for all times by a gay—Aye, by the God o' me!—
For all seasons! Done by the true Saint of Sodomy!"

I promised, and delivered on my promise.
What say you, Readers Dear, of this episode?
It has endurance, largesse, and surely no rhomb is
More perfectly proportioned. Scarce overload
Of details. All sublime. Modestly, no hecatomb is
Expected. Simple praise, as that bestowed
On Homer, Vir— "Poetaster, it takes a heavy toss
To find in your tale an iota of epic's *gravitas*.

We endured more than your hero—a buffoon,
Who o'ertips a buggered *Bedu*. Call you this
'Largesse,' equaling the generous-gestured boon
Of Achilles who with a bowing hand-kiss
Gave Priam Hector's body? And where is Don?
In distant Stanza 3, he was *y-clept* as
'Our Epyllion's gallant.' Here, he's measuring time
(Like a whore-house madam). And this you call 'sublime'?"

So that is what you wish. Why didn't you say so
Earlier? (I'll put aside all th'other
Faults you found, knowing that they all lay so
On your mind because the tale stressed another
While you wanted one of Don's.) Of Don's? . . . I may so
Happen to have one at hand. Aye, it will soothe or
Temper your tantrum, which grandly causes you to scrunch back
And sulk: A *conte* where Don's metamorphosed as hunchback.

(For since you treat my epic with a mock,
Mayhap my comic you'll raise to tragedy.
Who knows with readers, come down with readers' block?
Not that I call ye block-headed, though ye "be–",
That is, behead my epic in— "Tock-tick! Tick-Tock!"—
In its grand sweep, and strip to B.V.D.
Its heroic clo— "Epicist, desist, with your teary, oh-so
Caviling complaints. Remember *Orlando Furioso*

Is at hand. If we must be bored, that musty
Text takes precedence o'er your full-dull
Digressions. Proceed, proceed!" Your trusty
Epicist with earth-shaking Hordish Mogul
Speed complies.) Don'n'Harv,oure'erlusty
'Eroes,wej'in,astheyleis'lydownstroll
Alane'fAbha'soutskirts,cert'ntheirslummings
Eff'rtswo'bef'rnaught—"Epicist, drop the Cummings'

Forthwith!" (He-he)— "Uncertain," for it is Ramadan,
The month of abstinence in the Muslim calendar's
Swing. Harv spoke: "More chance to fuck the Dalai Lama, Don,
Than get a boy this blessed month, when every male indoors
Keeps his cock pure. I fear they'll be no ram o' Don
Or Harv tonight." He patted Don's arm. "My pal endures
His first grave Holy Month when every Mussulman
Spends all his time holy-fingering his Koran,

Not using digits to scratch his balls or clutch
At asshole hairs while sucking. Think of Greece!"
Indeed the lanes were bare as if a scrutch
Had pealed them clean; a slivered moon's release

Was scant, and leaned, as if upheld by crutch,
On the Atlas-laden night air, "dense as grease,"
Don shuttered. "Greece!" From homes and mosques, in holy heft,
Strange Allah-shrouded words circled like vultures, bereft

Of compassion. "I'd have to go back to Georgia
To find a scene less promising, more sulphurous,"
Don mewed. "And here you're horny as a Borgia,"
Harv's laugh broke in, "on an evening, dull for us,
And likely to get duller. Prayer done, they'll gorge a
Meal down, another, and if emerge won't suffer us
A glance. Their Ramadan ritual. We might as well head in."
They'd taken thirteen paces, when Harvey stopped. "A tread in

The darkness, not far behind us, I think I heard,"
He whispered, bending down to Don's right ear.
"Slow up. The sandals beat not only toward
Us, but down on us. . . Yes, Jaunt, a prey'r
Makes us his prey, you have it on my word."
Near became nearer, nearest, then "Mees-teer,
'Alo. I Ali." Both swung 'round and saw a bulwarks'
Youth, his face bean-plain. Don glanced downward, "At least,
        his tool works.

. . . In truth, it overworks," he added; "his mighty
Nightstick erects a Cheopsian pyramid
On his full-frontal *thobe*." With a highty-tighty
Grin, quite conscious his prick's reach did well exceed
His proffered hand, the youth sighed. "An Aphrodite
Pants o'er two aged Adonises, the mid

Points of their days well passed," Harv drolled. "E'er been so
     flattered,
Eh, Jaunt? (And this his Ramadan!) . . . I'm in a satyr-ed

Mood. You? Of course you are." Harv took the youth's hand
And squeezed, then his own let drift upon the limb
Below, which at its touch "seems—oh—to expand
E'en more, stretching the *thobe* 'yond any em
Its tailor set," Don gawked. With an underhand
Grasping hook, Harv towed the youth from the dim
Lane into a darker nook, some few five paces forwards.
Don caught some of their murmurings (for more and more words

Of Arabic he'd learned), enough to know
This Ali (not his real name Don was sure)
Wasn't dickering in their hushed to-and-fro
About *fluice* (money). It was pure amour
He was after. "Then why '*La! la!*' ['No! No!']
Keeps popping up?" Don asked himself. Soon Skewer
Alone stepped from the darkness, his face half-clad in grimace.
Don pouted, "Is he making some pert problems, the little trim ass?"

Harv coughed. "His father's sent him downtown, some *cumin*
Spice to get; can't be gone for mor'an 30 minutes;
So our flat's out. All alleys too: He has a human
Fear a passerby—understandable when it's
His neighborhood—might stumble by, see two men—
Kawadjahs [foreigners]—and him. Might ken, 'It's
Up to no good, these three are,' and raise such a 'Goddamnit!'
It'd turn Him over in his grave, the Prophet Mohammet.

[*Var. Sp.*, for that was how it was pronounced
By Skewer, your e'er attentive epicist
Quick interjects (always afraid I'll be pounced
On). That said, and before you can shout "Hist!"
I'll return to Harv, whose gloomy voice then bounced
Up, having bottom hit.] Hie! Jaunt, the tryst
You slobber for (and I), we'll have; Pseudonymous Ali
Knows a refuge, and if we don't dilly our dally

We're there in five minutes. It's a deserted
Building, reached by a straight uphill travail,
Which—Look, Jaunt!—he's already at." Alerted,
Don turned and caught only the swishing trail
Of the youth's flowing white *thobe*, as it skirted
The corner ahead. . . . Harv jawed on, "How comical
His two-sizes-too-large *thobe*! Like that dwarf from Disney's
Snow White— yes, Droopy! — like his cock which droops down
            to his knees,

Eh, Jaunt?. . . " Don but half listened, his eyes intent
On the crooked maze, "for the youth has lied, of course."
". . . Claustrophobic . . . stifles sex's instrument . . ."
The shacks had thinned out; the blacktopped lane's traverse
Had turned to a gravel path. ". . . by a circus tent
Smothered . . ." Ahead a mud building— ". . . And worse
. . . Reduced . . . apostrophic . . ."—surrounded by no bosk
To masque their entry— ". . . his grand—" "He's led us to a mosque!"

Don blurted. Harv's mumbles ceased, "Aye, the crescent
And minaret suggest he has. A most strange
Site for sex!" Don tensed; his mental stress sent
Chills through his body. "But no time to arrange

A" (Harv's eyes glanced down at his watch) "more 'pleasant
Seat,' to quote *Macbeth*'s Duncan, if it's a change
You seek, Jaunt." Don cursed. Harv smiled; casually he headed
Toward the youth. Don swore again. "The fool will get us beheaded

Or worse, be-penised before decapitation."
. . . Harv waved for him. Conscious that every eye
In each near house spied on his ambulation,
Don with uncertain tread crept forward. "Try
As I can to convince him, his explanation
O'erweighs. He says no rendezvousing risks lie
Within; this mosque's no longer used—kept as a relic—
Since the new one below was built, an Aristotelic

Syllogism, if ever I have heard one:
Prem. 1: Men pray in mosques. *Prem. 2*: Men prefer
The newer, better. *Conc.* (not an absurd one):
Men will be praying below. Logic doesn't err,
Jaunt. This shrine's safe for sex. Upon my word, one
Safer could not be found. Before you demur,
I'll tighten the enthymeme: Myself I will stand guard at
This portal; if e'en a mouse moves—while you are hard at

His cock—in our mosquely direction, I'll whistle
(And you must vow to do the same for me),
Giving you both full time to gain dismissal
From love's trap, and fly. In the generosity
I'm noted for, I'll let you first 'gnaw gristle.'"
Don stalled, and would have kept this pendency
Had not from inside the mosque come a guttural "*Yallah!*
[Quickly!]" . . . With wavering steps, Don entered the
　　　House of Allah,

Hearing as a "plaintive anthem" Skewer's "Five
Minutes only." The room was small, but one pillar
Held up its tapered ceiling, "like a beehive
Shaped," observed Don. "And its walls hold no frill or
Decor, save windows two, through which arrive
More moonbeams than I'd expected as mosque-filler."
"*Yallah!*" hallooed a voice from behind the once-muck column.
"I come, my Ali [for what else do I have to call 'im,

Don reasoned], my Ali, I come," his response
In Arabic. . . . "'*Tempus non fugit* when you're
Having fun,'" Don mused, knowing that his ounce
Of time had become a pound. A stewing Skewer
Would greet him, curse him, *in toto* renounce
Their friendship true for taking twice—nay truer—
Thrice his allowed five. "I'll put the blame on Ali, 'who
Wouldn't let me stop, Harv,' pleading with much broguish
　　　ballyhoo."

. . . "*Assalamu-alaikum.* [Peace.]" "Could that voice
Be Harv's?" Don panicked. "But it sounds so hoary."
In mid-fuck, Ali had frozen. "I rejoice
To find a second come to pray in the Glory
Of this Old Survivor." Don's sweat, as choice
As Ali's, began to flow, . . . nigh on Christ's gory
Perspiration. A swooning drop, and Don was covered
By Ali's circus-tented *thobe.* "Step forth! Why stay hovered

Behind that pillar? Allah's all-righteous man
Has reason none to hide," (Much of the Arabic
Don weened) "for surely a son of the Koran
You show you are, by coming on this—" ("I'm sick

And getting sicker," Don groped.)— "1 Ramadan
To a tumbling down mosque, always my pick
On this day" (like a monkey seeking a higher branch,
Don began to scale Ali's buttocks, back), "thereby to stanch

And shrive the sins I've spent a year enrobing
My self and soul. . . . It was the mosque of my youth.
'Twas yours? Come out—for you've set me a-sobbing
To see you—or you'll force me the hounded sleuth
To become." (In undergarment fear, with globing
Grasps, Don clutched Ali's chest). "In this House of Truth
Thou'rt truly known." (Don heard two sandals slide. "Cardiac
Arrest, set in! Ali's stepping forth, toting me piggyback!")

"Ah, now I understand why you do hide,"
The old voice stammered. "Come, we'll prayer together,
Knowing there's always a Third at our side,
O'erpeeping our back. It matters not whether
Our bodies are hale. 'Tis Soul that dost abide!"
His voice trailed off, but a hand as a tether
Fell on Don's back and tugged. Ali spoke, "Graybeard grandsire,
I must go, my prayers finished. May Allah find in His pow'r

To forgive my sins," his words like a rabbit's squeak.
In procession, Ali moved on. "May Allah lean
O'er your sad shoulders e'er. God, bless the meek,
The downtrodden, guide them through every pain
The body endures," the old man called. A week
It seemed to Don before they reached the lane
That fronted the mosque. Ali set to running, heedless
Of the 155-lb. bundle he bore. Needless

To say, Don's lightened conscience also scurried.
A-sudden Ali stopped, and with a shiver
Dropped Don, who heard a thunder blast, a flurried
Lightning flash saw. Anon a yellow river
With mud-rich clogs swept o'er his face and hurried
Through his clothes. Don saw and said, "Well did you ever?
I'm shit and pissed upon." The fleeing youth cried out,
"Abadan! Wallahi! Ma fee, tanni!" (A round-about

Translation: "Never, by God, that again!")
Don glanced around and saw he had been dumped
In an alley. "So these are the wages of sin!"
He sighed, but no *"Abadan"* ("Never") trumped
Don's exclamation. He found some half-clean
Papers close by and began to pick the clumped
Strings of runny shit from his shirt. And that was when
He asked, "Where was Harv's whistle? Damn, I've been
          humped, twice humped,

Because he slacked his guard. Some friend, some pal!"
He sprinkled some dust over the slurred urine.
"None untruer than Harvey Skewer! Ne'er shall
I trust him. '*Jamais plus*! Here's manure in
Your eye,' I'll greet him." Using a nearby wall,
Don pushed himself up. When he felt secure in
His balance, he set out for their car. "At least, it's downhill.
. . . The S.O.B.! After seeing me as besmeared as a clown, he'll

Make some cruel joke, for sure." . . . The sedan came into
His fuzzy view (for o'er his eyelids piss's
Crystals had salt-settled). Yet nothing akin to
Skewer's bulk he saw. "One of his artifices:

He's hidden inside, crouched up like some Shinto
Denizen at prayer. I'll show him where the bliss is
In tricking a friend." With both fists clenched, Don peeped in,
But found the floorboard bare. An hour passed: Seeped–in

Revenge seeped out, as Skewer did not appear.
"Perhaps some neighbor saw him standing guard,
Alone and trusty, outside the mosque; that o'erseer
Alerted the police, who swooped down hard
And fast. Ever the faithful cavalier,
My friend did hoist upon his own petard
Himself, thus saving me. Not like Christ's false friend who
        petered out,
When confronted, my Harv ne'er once faltered, ne'er
        teetered. Out

Of the mosque's yard, he got them—to protect
. . . Ah me, poor me." Don wept at this climaxed low point
To which his thoughts had taken him. Abject,
He fell upon the car's hood. "At no point
In the torture he now fronts—though they direct
Blows on his person—does he with finger slow point
At, or implicate, me." He conjured up the "out-Spanishing"
Inquisition his friend endured. But that nightmare,
        vanishing

More quickly than it had come, yielded to a mirage,
When, looking up, Don thought he saw his Harv
Loping down the hill, calm in his steerage
And humming a light tune. . . . "It helps to carve
The air like a maestro when you hum, clearage
Allowed," Harv piped. "Don't want a high note's swerve

To hit a low-lying branch." Don's anger had passed mere rage:
"You bastard! To lilt an aria of Verdi takes some nerve

When through your faithlessness I've been all-shit
Upon, pissed o'er. Ne'er has a falser sentry
Stood watch!" Don cried. "Now that you mention it,
Phew! You need a shower. Make that the first entry
On the *do* side of your *do-don't* chit."
Harv stopped to grin. "'5 minutes' . . . Had there been tree
To lean against or bench to sit upon, perhaps, aye, my time
Would have more gaily passed, and I'd have opted to buy time

And overtime for you, but there were none.
By the way, in the mosque were you all-sullied
Or was it afterwards, during the run?"
Harv waited as Don sputtered, his tongue dull lead.
In time, coherent words—though not the benison
Type at first—came forth: ". . . Once more the gullied
Cully I am! If you saw us in our speedy exit,
How could you miss the old man's entry, not try to vex it?

And where was your vaunted warning whistle?" No pause
In Harv's reply: "I did!—to address the first
Of your two questions. I howdied him; soon our jaws
Were exchanging pleasantries. He even thrust
His arm in mine (Othello's 'It is the cause,
It is the cause, my soul' with clarion burst
Filled my mind) as I led him to the mosque's sacred portals."
("You ushered!" gasped Don.) "Shakespeare, his words do
          make us mere mortals

Less 'mortal,' less 'mere.' We summon his *esprit*,
And ne'er does his ghost fail when called upon.
E.g.'s: His *Tempest* tells us 'misery'
Makes 'strange bed-fellows'; his *Merchant* gets some fun
From a sand-blind old father. You follow me,
Jaunt? . . . Am I accoutred like a Mussulman?
That old one hailed me as 'Brother,' complimented my *thobe*'s
Fine cloth and hang. 'Tis then I knew he saw with near-dimmed
        globes.

That is 'the cause' I let him enter, guided
His steps even. Had there been a Saturnalian
Orgy in progress, he'd seen its many-sided
Sexual poses as the fixed universalian
Islamic genuflections and would have presided
As their *imam* [prayer leader], without an alien
Unholy afterthought. So you were ne'er in danger.
A pleasing jest— '5 min.'—eh Jaunt, sly wolf of the manger?"

Harv stopped, but not to gauge if Don approved.
He stepped back. "Our Ramadan breeze has shifted,"
Spoken after a gag. "Your odor's shoved
Up my nostrils, down into my belly." He drifted
Aft five paces more. "I'll continue, having moved
Out of nose-shot: I've spent the last hour, gifted
With the old man's wisdom. His final words come, in a clump,
        back
To me: "There goeth I (or thee), in that [hightailed] humpback!"

Harv's boff roared. "Not in the stars of his twinkling eyes,
The fault is," a dazed Don mused. "I am the ruer

For o'erreaching. I satyr fell, to satirize
My own-earned plight. No more I'll evil do or
Think, where Harv's concerned." And so with that wise
Lesson learned, our hero, intoning "None truer
Etc.," offered his right hand to Harv—who quick disdained the
          prize
As "shitty." . . . We close, Don hurling manure at H. Skewer.

"We close" means not we close. Such sudden stop
Ill-rounds the epic off. Though there's symmetry
In Don's progress from fetal to fecal slop,
I'll use another; as Nature does trim a tree
From the forest, thus freeing some underprop
To see the sun, so I will use such mimicry
And give you, my readers—each metamorphosed as seedling—
A sneak preview of what Greece holds, your irksome needling

Throughout my epic being put aside
Charitably. For 'tis to Greece our heroes
Are bound (both Harv and Don so specified
Some 30 stanzas prior). "Aye, our year rows
By so fast," Harv had announced; "an ebb-tide
Nips Arabia's Academe, nigh on ground zero's
Terminus. Jaunt, your ass's been stuffed with, your tongue has spun
'Round, circumcised cocks only. . . . Let's try Greece's *un*-."

It had been settled fast. To Athens' hills
They'd fly for holiday: To taste the smegmatic
Delights of foreskins unsnipped; seize the thrills
Of finding spots where Socrates sucked an Attic

Stripling, where Plato was poked, and Aristotle's
Zunge reamed lesser assholes, in peripatetic
Practice for Alex. the Great's. They'll double-time to Sparta—
Your "Ahem!" quickens my pace—there learn how to part a

Tight crack without drawing blood. Such swift sword play
Don'll master, bating not or holding sloppily
In check his wants. And Harv will with a horde play,
Each Greek youth falling—as at Thermopylae
Their ancients did—upon his spear. . . . My word play
Must soar to Olympian heights, no line choppily
Hewn, to capture this. O Muse, inspire so that my pen is—
What? You readers speak? "Since you won't, we'll use the word,

'Finis'"

PORTRAIT OF A STATUE
AS A (VERY) YOUNG MAN

". . . to coax out of flesh the marble that is hidden in it."

Patrick White, *Voss*

"Sculpted like a David, why would he want to become a Michelangelo?" Withers whispered into my right ear.

The tic of his head, emphatic at the chin, had already directed me toward the worktable on the right side of the Art Lab. There two girls lulled their bodies against the third student—the young man Withers had telephoned me about last night—whose hands, having smoothed, began a tentative shaping of the clay.

"Handsome," I understated. In being turned, my chin tapped Harold's right cheek.

"And talented in his hands. So talented he's used up all my use to him, which he announced last night." Never taking his eyes from the mass of clay, the young man pulled back his body and took in what seemed to me all of the air about the table, causing not only his chest but also his arms below the sleeveless T-shirt to swell.

"What will it be?" one of the girls asked, lifting her left arm and placing it on his right collarbone.

"If only my hands could think." The voice sounded hurt, as if protesting against the amercement; he shook the arm from his shoulder before leaning his elbows against the table, cradling his chin, and beginning a brown study of the lump of clay.

Harold did not speak during the walk from the building that housed the Visual Arts section of our university over to Liberal Arts where my office was. However, the catbird-seat smile never left his face, not even after he took a sip from the cup of stale coffee I had poured.

"You took the lead with him, I suppose," knowing from his *sub-rosa* affectation on the telephone that he would wait for me to begin.

"In fact, it was the other way around. It was Christmas night at Man's Kingdom." He stared at me defiantly, knowing I did not like his going to that bar of "rough trading." "Why shouldn't I? You and Neils had flown off to Jamaica for the Christmas break." "Not asking me," he did not add, knowing Neils had been the reason.

"There were twelve or so of us there, familyless and seeking not to spend Christmas night friendless, each waiting for the arrival of something through the oak entrance, but we were low—bumping against empty—on faith. The door opened and all eyes shot toward the light let in, the silhouette of the young man gaining instant approval.

"As the door closed, he adjusted his eyes to the half-darkness. And then it seemed he was walking toward me; a panicky rosiness set in, 'Why the God is he choosing me?' But he apparently was, for he stopped in front of my mostly-turned stool.

"'Professor Withers,' he announced, rather than inquired. I could not take my eyes from his white–neon–revealed face—why should I be different from everyone else in the bar?—but made no acknowledgment of who I was. 'I want to be a sculptor. To work in marble.' Not pausing, he placed an artist sketchbook onto the fake-marble top of the counter. 'You will see my sketches.'

"Reluctantly, I brought my eyes from his face, but having looked saw the talents of his artist hand, a charcoal sketch of a just-hatched dove, the drawing high-lighted on its one visible eye, filled with the chiaroscuro of fright and love—of 'terrible beauty' being born—at confronting the world for its first time.

"The shuffling of six feet interrupted my scrutiny. 'Withers,

Withers,' the triplets chirped, 'Introduce, introduce us to your Christmas present. We come bearing gifts.' A beer, a highball, and a gin on rocks were placed in front of him. Their eyes, I saw, were carving him up. 'Are you for the unwrapping?' the most-forward of the three leaned toward him and asked.

"His hand seized the beer, downed it, then the second and third drink, without a seeming break. I could see that he wished me to answer. 'Ye three Marys, we are speaking of sculpting —carving in stone, not carving up life.' I spit my ready venom toward them, causing each to jump back.

"But the words also seemed to have the same effect on him, as if they were repulsive to, the archenemy of, his nature. 'I have registered for your Sculpture 105 class.' His hand snatched the sketchbook. 'I will see you after the Christmas break.'

"As he hurried toward the door, I called out weakly, 'Wait. Wait. I will go with you.' But I had been unable to rise from my stool. I spent a lonely, unannunciated Christmas night, in truth the whole holiday, the first time I've ever been in a hurry for one to end."

Withers sighed, rose, and walked toward the coffee maker. "I need not have worried," he continued from there, "for, Martin, as you will find, he is 'good to his word.'"

He saw me lean forward and correctly interpreted my anticipation of how he had proceeded. "The usual way. Brush-stroked a hand against his crotch the second day of class. When he did not seem—pretended not, I told myself at the time—to notice, I asked him over that night. Got him to the sofa, where I settled in against him, my head barely reaching his shoulders. He had the brandy and soda held rigidly in his semi-clasped hands—gay-fright, I thought—as my left hand slid under the glass and rested on the copper buttons of his jeans.

"Not looking down toward me, he spoke purposively, 'I am but young in the experience of this world. You must further my sculpting technique,' but you know how the young slur their speech these days, and 'further' came out as 'father.' I had begun the unbuttoning, but noticed he had not sucked in his stomach to make my task easier. 'Tell me about my predecessors, all my fathers'—this time enunciated clearly. 'You may break chronology this night by talking first of Michelangelo.' By then my hand was in, struggling to dislodge and get his thing out—as overweening as the 'third leg' on a male Mali wooden figurine."

"'In the jeans the hands come and go / Talking of Michelang—'" My burst of laughter cut short the garbled quote from Eliot. Withers tried not to redden. I continued: "God knows, man, we're now beginning the fourth week of the semester, and you mean to say—in fact, you implied it on the telephone last night—you haven't got any further, . . . father."

"Last night he stopped me at Brancusi. From before Phidias to Rosso's 'Only the play of light [on the stone] matters.'" Withers paused while the words seemed to be being chomped on. "Thirty centuries, and you say I haven't got far. In time, at least."

He heaved, to indicate the frustration of besieging a party who would not take notice he was under siege. "As long as I kept talking—lecturing, really—he didn't seem to mind what I did with my hands. But that was all I was allowed to do, until last night. That first night, after I had it out and in hand—as much in thrall as Michelangelo's 'Bound Slave,' of which I was lecturing—I dropped my head towards his crotch, certain my tongue could erect what my hand had been unable to. He placed his on the bald spot of my head, and it seemed to cleave as he uplifted me. 'I don't think you can lecture with your mouth full.'"

A second hurtful burst of laughter pealed from my throat, and although Harold did not join in, a self-mocking, appreciative twinkle came to his eyes. Eight years ago, my third day at Palm Cove University, this balding man in his early forties, dressed in a smock covered with paint and clay splotches, had sat down opposite me in the cafeteria. "I'm Harold Withers, sculptor, and as such I've been sizing you up. We must get acquainted before the dew dissolves." That night we had, probably on the same spot as the "bound slave" of whom he was talking—I suddenly realized I didn't even know his name. A one-time stand, which we both had agreed immediately would be the last.

We enjoyed gossiping, and in the intervening years, Harold had shifted quite a few transients over to me, the only kind he likes, although he won't admit it. Two years ago— "The game is afoot again; I tire of him."—he had sent over Neils. And I had retired from the field. Neils had not, and thinking of that had been enough to cut short my laugh.

I waited a bit and retook it up. "Harold, your fingers have lost their touch!" And to show I was neither ashamed nor afraid to bring Neils in, I added, "Neils frequently swears yours could get a rise out of a deadman."

"I'm not sure whether Hylas is dead or alive. Does a tree make a sound in the forest if no one is there to hear its fall?" He returned to his chair, his cup of coffee half drunk before the coffee maker. "Last night he did the dumping and made inquiries of you. I had introduced Brancusi with his pronouncement, 'Your hand thinks and follows the thought of the stone.' His right hand shot roughly upward, seized the scruff of my neck, and shoved my head downward toward where my hands fondled. For the first time my lips touched his flesh, and I knew I was through.

"He snapped, 'He is wrong. Hands think, but Stone does not think. I am antithetical to—the antithesis of—the abstract. He is wrong.' And he, who had seldom spoken during our three weeks together, muttered I am sure much of the same under-the-breath protestations during the next five minutes. Then, those two hands—a sculptor's hands I instinctively knew at their one previous touch—cupped my head and lifted it not ungently from his crotch.

"He stood up, walked toward the door, and, having already

buttoned up his coppers, began, 'I have used up too much of your time.' Not meaning, I realized as I sank further into the sofa, the polite, 'I've taken up too much of your time,' but the truthful, 'I've used up all the time I've allotted to you.' He continued, 'You have a friend, Professor Martin Didache.' He didn't ask. *He never asks,*" and the words seemed to be choking Harold, "but I knew what I was expected to do. He was out at 8:15, and I was on the phone with you at 8:16. At the open door, his final words had been, 'You will not forget me. I would not be forgotten.'"

Harold got up, and as if imitating the actions of the one of whom he was speaking, walked to, opened the door, and positioned himself in the sunlight of its aperture. "His first name is Todd. Eighteen, I approximate, what *you* call a (very) young man, but his exact answer was 'Too young. I want to be older, to work in marble.' That's about all I got from him. However, you might want to—need to—know how he reacted to my three-week history of sculpture up to the Modern Abstract:

"The unsignatured primitives widened his eyes; the idealized Greeks stopped his breathing; he stifled a yawn as I spoke of the realistic Romans, sniffed at the Byzantines, but when we reached fifteenth-century Italy a saint's transport took over his face. He strained with the Baroques, and his penis seemed to diminish—if that word can ever be used of it—when we reached the Rococo. The Romantics caused him to emit at several points an embarrassed cough, and as I spoke of Rodin and the early Moderns he seemed to be consciously scratching an unconscious itch."

Withers was swinging the door at its handle. "He's yours. You're more the Pygmalion type, capable of the patience needed to bring a statue to life. Surely you must be tiring of Neils."

Harold was already three paces from the door when I shouted I wasn't, and thought so too.

It was the momentary alarm I saw enter Neils' eyes as I withdrew my lips from his that convinced me I had perhaps lied.

To me it was the same kiss I had given him for the past two years, the first thing I did when I came into our house, although sometimes, especially of late, I had wanted to start in on cleaning the mess he, or some of the friends I knew he had over while I was at work, had spent the day making.

Neils' response was immediate; drawing upon a twenty-six-year instinct—implanted I was sure when he came from his mother's womb—pulling me down toward him with his left arm, and with his right hand taking out his penis, shot up with the suddenness of a geyser—for when I had bent over to kiss him, there was the barest of an imprint on the jockey shorts—he mumbled: "I wanna sc'ew."

The next day, I was exiting through the front entrance of the Liberal Arts Building, not thinking—I am certain—of "this" Todd but of Neils, frantically at me yesterday afternoon. His alarm had become dread, I sensed. I chuckled, certain the house would be cleaned, at least half-cleaned, and for sure no friends would have been over, when I arrived after twenty minutes.

Hylas must have shifted his body, for I glanced toward the side wall and saw him, dressed in the same blue jeans and white T-shirt of yesterday. The two girls of the Lab room had been joined by a third, but I noticed he did not reply to their disappointed goodbyes. I quickly put something together—all right, maybe I had put something together while Neils was at me yesterday, but it wasn't fixed in stone. However, it wasn't necessary.

Of course, I *had* stopped, but it was he who walked over and spoke, fixing his body firmly a pace from me, "Hello, you were talking to Dr. Withers yesterday, outside the Lab. I took you in over the clay I was studying. That's why I'm not a sculptor yet; I take in too much of the periphery. You can help me not do that, I am sure, being a professor, Dr. Didache, of literature."

2

"Emulating your namesake—the Catholic Saint, Martin, not the Disagreeable German—have you stretched yourself at full length upon the 'stone dead' and brought it to life?" My mind conjured up the "specialty" of the Catholic hermit which had garnered him sainthood. Withers' good-natured guffaw, delighting in itself, transubstantiated through the phone wires.

"Am I or is he the quick? the dead?" I answered, although it might be argued that I asked.

"Didache, it is just like you, wanting it both ways," he whispered, as if my ear were next to his mouth, punning as he had done several times before upon my family name. His voice rose with a sigh. "Poor Neils! (Poor Me!) He continues—what is it one week now?—to pound me with a vengeance, each stroke resurrecting my hemorrhoids," he giggled quietly. "Revenge cries out— against you? against Hylas? against the circumstances of the universe?—bloody revenge. In place and on time—Ouch! Ouch!—I am rammed raw! Won't you tell Hylas to hurry up and finish with you, so you can again take Neils off of my hands, out of my asshole hair?"

I thought, after I had hung up without an answer or a "Goodbye," that *in time* it had been Neils out, Todd in, but *in place* it had been the reverse. Timewise, Todd had decided it over coffee that first afternoon: "I will move in with you," he had announced, not "Do you want me to move in?" or even "I want to move in." So even before I—preoccupied not with rehearsing what I would say to Neils, but with how the second bedroom could be converted into a workshop for Todd—stumbled over two suitcases as I stepped across the threshold of my place, the decision had been made, timewise.

Neils sat rigidly on the sofa, his face scrunched up by his angry eyes, transfixed beyond my shoulders on the door. His body was excessively clothed, as novel to me as it must have been for him, my not having rushed straight home from the university to begin my eight-hour pampering regime. He rose. In the clothes, his body, at its full length, looked more massive, and (I will confess) a tinge of rue squiggled across my mind, like an operating-room blip, that I had known him almost wholly in the nude.

He stomped past me, careful not to brush, snapping, "Ain't puttin' up this shit." I still had not risen from my knees onto which I had tumbled. With one hand, he seized the separate straps of the bags, bringing them together, and dragged the perch on which I had alit from under me, tossing me onto the carpet.

At the doorway, however, I noticed a slight pause between the turning of the knob and the opening of the door, time and place enough for me to cry out something. But I did not. Not looking toward me, his eyes intent on the knob, he grimaced, "I'm splittin'."

That word is probably as good a "segue" as I will get. Todd and I are in bed; it is three days after the slab of Carrara marble had arrived—almost a week after Withers had told me to urge Todd to hurry up and finish with me, to take Neils out of his hairs, to portmanteau his two expressions for the sake of brevity. I had just completed my last desperate attempt to brighten Todd's eyes, downcast in thought since the Carrara had come.

"Splitting Adam," he cried out, it having dawned on him what I had just said, the rounding off of my narration of the Antaeus myth with the commentary: "I've always thought that when Hercules uplifted Antaeus—separating him from his mother earth Terra—was the first instance of man splitting the atom." He struck his head towards mine, with all the zero-to-the-bone suddenness of a snake's lash, and pitted his against my lips . . . for the first time.

"The tables are turned," I am sure you are thinking, remembering my slur about Harold's centuries-long snail's pace in wooing Hylas. Consider, however, at least, we slept together, something Harold never got. In fact, I had free run of his body, but before that night he had never bent to kiss me, never dropped a hint to indicate he cared if I were there, never—how shall I say it?—swelled to a passion. "Dead stone? stone dead?" you might ask, but I never did.

I know I'm skipping around, and you might surmise (without any censure from me) that I can not confront the chronological and spatial order of what happened. Nothing could be further from the truth, and to prove this I'll "segue" that kiss with the Carrara.

Neils exited in the afternoon, and Todd was encamped that night. The next morning on the breakfast table in front of the chair where I took my coffee was an art journal folded over to a page of advertisements. I immediately seized on the one which was meant for me: "White Carrara marble, 4' x 4' $500"; delivery would be made within ten days. I jotted down the toll-free number.

"My boy will have his marble," I glee-clubbed. (I hear you, like Eliot's Eternal Footman, "snicker," ye who prefer Shakespeare's, not Ovid's, rendition of Pyramus/Thisbe. To be truthful, I present myself now as *less* ridiculous than I actually was then.)

He never spoke of it—the magazine was gone when I came in that afternoon. Waiting. Waiting. I was aware of the waiting, but he continued to get his workshop ready. By day four he had the pinewood floor cemented over; the next five days the edifice began to rise and rise—a giant table of cement, the base on which he would sculpt his Carrara, "and not unlike, I am sure, the altar the Aztecs used for carving up virgins during their blood rites. By the way, have I given you my daily medical report? Neils wants your blood or Hylas's, and gets mine," Withers grumbled.

It came on 6 February. It was my usual 2:41 when I came in; pieces of the crate were flung across the living room. "He had torn into the box—he-he," I giggled; "what will he do to me?"

Actually, nothing. I did not know that, so I jigged—on air—towards the workroom. The white square had been placed at the center of the cement slab, but I took it in as periphery, for he had stripped off his clothes, and with his well-formed buttocks pointed toward the door was leaned over the stone mound, his chin in his hands, gazing toward it.

When he did not respond to what I said—I've forgotten what I did say—I crept over and began to nibble on his shoulders. I worked down to his buttocks and slipped myself under, meeting first his scrotum and edging apace—my eyes still as closed as his I was sure were open—moved my lips upward, wondering, dreaming, how long my tongue would have to "labor" before my parched throat would be lymphatically moistened. (Sickening, isn't it, what apotheosizing will do to one's syntax?)

Alas, my nose was the first to stumble on the truth—the limp mass—and simultaneous with the touch came words which sank through the thick cement slab, "Now what will I make of you, my beauty?" And I found out the bitter truth: He would ask of his marble.

There followed the picking of my brain for three nights. I quickly realized that Withers had given him only the facts and technique of art, none of the spirit. My (Proust's) "to seize, isolate, immobilize for the duration of a lightning flash," I was sure, put a Malrauxian "gleam" in his eyes, although the bed from which we spoke was always in a room all dark. It was M. Andre Malraux himself who worked best—and yes, I passed his and everyone else's ideas off as my own.

I rested my head across his navel and quoted, rather paraphrased: "Goya's monsters seem to remember they were once humans." I sensed he was trying to work something out.

"The obverse is also true, but that is better than the obverse," he finally commented.

It was Malraux's "The devil, who always paints in two dimensions, has become the most eminent artist of our time" which set us off on the night I second-most remember. I had prefaced this by saying, *op. cit.* M. Andre, that the artist works in a world in which he is God.

There was no hesitation, as always before, in his response, as if there was nothing to be worked out. "I must go beyond the Devil"—his voice seemed to capitalize the word, which I was certain had not been done by Malraux—"beyond God."

"Into chaos . . . through blood and darkness." I was trying to remember what Malraux had written exactly, and got confused. Confusion breeds confusion; Andre's "antidestiny" came out as "antipredestination" and his "Art does not deliver man from being only an accident in the universe" became "Art does not deliver the universe from being only a man in the accident." I tried to recover by making a weak joke, "Before God, Todd."

I perceived a smile of approval. He yawned, "Now we must find the myth that will turn that into flesh."

(It was only later—just last Tuesday, he had been gone for eight weeks—that I came across Djuna Barnes' "flesh that will become a myth." By then, I was surprised neither by his having "chanced" on her key words nor by his having rendered them *vice versa.*)

The next day at 2:41, he approached with a book from my library and an assertion: "Myth is a clipped form of mythology. Here." It was *Bulfinch's*, and I knew what I had to do. A "Scheherazade" of fables unwound that night, the word being Withers' the next day. "Does that mean you've got him for a thousand and one? My asshole can't take it, you selfish bastard!"

"Well, throw Neils out," I exasperated.

"But where will he go? He'll storm over there and murder you or Hylas or both, and then I'll have your blood—I don't care about Hylas's—on my hands. Better a bloody ass than bloody hands." The phone receiver was slammed down—by him.

So we come to Antaeus and Hercules. I'll quote the story as Bulfinch tells it:

> A celebrated exploit of Hercules was his victory over Antaeus. Antaeus, the son of Terra, the Earth, was a mighty giant and wrestler, whose strength was invincible so long as he remained in contact with his mother Earth. . . . Hercules encountered him, and finding that it was no avail to throw him, for he always rose with renewed strength from every fall, he lifted him up from the earth and [crushed the life out of] him in the air.

"Splitting the atom . . . Splitting Adam . . . Smack." Good ole Bulfinch had gotten me an unexpected, a procreative kiss. What would the finished statue get me, I checkled, carrying my pre-sleep dream into my sleep? I never considered that I would lose him, once the statue was finished. In fact, technically I did not, as you will find out.

The following day I rushed to the workroom and bent over the shoulders of his hunched-forward naked body. The most detailed and exquisite penciled sketch of two nude young men I had ever seen stared back at me. One had the other grasped around the waist and lifted, so that the penis of the second dangled across the bridge of the nose of the uplifter. I had no sooner pecked him on his left collarbone than his right hand dropped the pencil and both hands tore the artist paper from the pad and ripped it to pieces.

I jumped back, startled by the violence. The face that turned towards me was full of pain, "Of course, you don't see. They are both me, the two I draw. I am diffusing the life from myself!" He rushed from the room in terror.

The next three days, when I came in to inspect, the scene was basically repeated, but I noticed before he tore it that each day brought less detail. His conception of Antaeus uplifted was disappearing, his arms first, then his head, then his torso, then his legs, and on the third day the penis which had lolled above Hercules' nose. It was as if he waited for me to come and in his destroying each sketch before my eyes wished to convey to me the impasse he had reached. The periphery had been gotten rid of, but it had left himself only with his self, sufficient for himself, I realized, but not for his art.

I was helpless to help him, I felt, and when he did not leave his workroom to come to my bed that night, I was resigned that I must lose him.

Again, wrong, for the moment.

"This," he demanded, rushing towards me even before the front door had begun to close, his cock waddling between his thighs.

"He was a friend of mine . . . before, Todd," I answered as I looked at the photograph of Neils, playing volleyball on the beach, the only one of him I had not burned. I didn't question how he had found my hiding place; after all, he had dug up *Bulfinch* somehow.

"You will get him—my Antaeus." He turned and marched towards the workroom, closed and locked the door. I sulked and slept alone a fourth night, although I little slept.

"I know'd it's yah. Whatja want?" Neils growled into the phone, although the question had a sprouting bud of mildness.

"Would you like to earn a hundred dollars for maybe thirty minutes of work?" I tried to make my voice sound both pleasant and businesslike.

"I ain't no pros'tute, come o'e'feh thi'ty min'tes a day. What, his cock done play'dout?"

I started to explain it would be just a one-timer, but decided against. "Well, if you wish, be over at 8:30 tonight." I hung up before he could reply, never doubting that he would come.

Long before the doorbell rang, the camera had been readied—I was to be the photographer. Todd paced from the bedroom, in the nude; on his return, I could not see Neils behind him, although he is half a head taller than Todd. He was there, but had diminished himself.

Although I had not, and had told him I had not, Todd began, "Martin has told you what we're going to do. Strip off your clothes."

Neils let out a gulp, cut it short, and seeming to have resigned himself that he had put his name on the contract simply by coming, began to unbutton his shirt, eying the camera I held or peeping toward Todd, but never once fixing his eyes on mine.

Todd canvassed Neils, now in his bare. "You've let yourself go a little bit since the photograph, but no matter. I can compensate. After all, I am a sculptor. We don't need a rehearsal, just a talk-through. *Ars est celare artem.* Come here. I will lift you up. You really have little to do, except be lifted up. You're Antaeus, I'm Hercules. Antaeus got his strength from his Mother Earth; every time Hercules threw him to the ground his Mother—Terra or Terror, whatever—pumped him up with renewed vigor. So how could Hercules kill him? Answer, boy."

"I dunno" came, after a quick scratch at his left testicle, but I could see that Neils was eager to have the answer. He had got into the game, and wasn't planning to leave until he had learned something he could use.

"Why, old chum—and if you hadn't reached for your left ball, I'm sure you would have figured it out—by uplifting him and squeezing the life out while holding him in the air. Try to put on your face that same pained expression you now have, but if it leaves you, no matter, I'm a sculptor. As for your arms, listen closely. Martin explained this to me. [Of course, I had not.] You've given up trust in your body, so you've stopped pounding

Hercules' back. Your hands—an outreach of your soul—should be straining toward Terra/Terror, you know like one of those wrestlers in a tag team match trying to stretch to slap-hand his partner in. You want to tag your Mother in. Got that."

"Yah n'tgonna hu't me, kill me, a'e yah?" Neils said, finally fish-eying me.

"Only in the sculpture. Here let me muss your hair; you've been fighting for six hours or so, assuming Greek legends relied on our system of time, my man." He tousled Neils' hair with his artist hand.

"I'll t'ke m' 'unde'd b'fo'e, ifyah please." He glowered at Todd, but I knew it was meant for me.

"Where will you put it, old sod? Have you forgotten you're in the buff?" The rhetorical questions aside, Todd put an arm around Neils' rosy neck and drew him close so that their bodies almost touched. I realized two things, as I, clutching the Polaroid, walked to my point: In five minutes, Neils had gotten twice the overtures I had been gifted in three weeks, and two, that Neils' penis was beginning to unshrivel ever so slightly. "Dear God," I prayed, "don't let me lose him to him," certain at the time of the proper antecedent of each pronoun (but not so certain now).

"You're ready, Martin." It wasn't asked, so I didn't reply.

Todd bent at his knees, reached his arms around Neils at the small of his back, and pressed his chin against Neils' navel, having already sucked a ton (I exaggerate) of air into his body. It lunged upward and Neils' ascended, like an Arion from its launchpad, and like the man-made Space Age marvel it began to tilt after its initial rise, edging inward at the same time as Todd's chin slid down. The friction seemed to make Neils' penis begin to swell. In the final surge, it had wedged itself under Todd's chin, and he breathed into its pubic hair. "Now," Todd screamed. "Now, you son of earth."

As soon as he heard the click, he relaxed his grip of Neils' body, which did not fall in a plop to the floor, but rather slurred across Todd's, his chest and face slithering downward, crossing and smearing the "cum" on Todd's chest.

From below, a defiant protest came, "Yah 'most b'oke m' back, yah ..." Neils stammered, searching for an insult, but failed to find, and settled on emending the last he had heard, "yah no sona ea'th!"

Todd did not answer immediately. Showing the fingers of his right hand, he rebuffed with similar accusation, "*You* 'came' on my chest."

"Yah squeez'd 'toutame," after almost a quarter of a minute, Neils responded, pushing himself up from the floor and massaging his lower back.

The *schumpp* of the Polaroid had been lost in their philistine-driven bickering. Todd saw the print lodged in its slot, "hung out and dried"; he lurched forward and seized it, his hand overtaking mine. As he gazed on it, I saw the Malrauxian "gleam" come into his eyes—the one I had imagined in the darkness.

Neils also saw. He scoffed, "W'll I'm glad't cam'out, 'cause I'm't goin' th'ough tha' 'gain. Gimme m' 'unde'd—"

Todd, suddenly, had grabbed me by the neck and pushed his mouth against mine, the sudden passion causing me to drop the Polaroid, which as it hit the carpet sent off a rattling, "Well, I'm no more of use."

Neils' next speech was again cut off, begun just as Todd withdrew his lips and stopped when Todd let fall his arms, uplifted me, and threw me onto the center of the bed. "I'm splittin', a 'und—"

"The right. The left." Todd had not looked towards Neils; his eyes ticked off the two sections of the bed, in which I was the Golgothan center.

"I wan' th'und—" Neils was again drawn short by a sharp turn of Todd's head.

"Th' ... lef', ... the left," he stuttered.

Todd stepped to the switch and batted it down, meaning that his reply was filtered through a dark room, "Good. I wanted—but you knew that—the right."

[*N. P.* Insert here all of Poe's "Descent into the Maelstrom."]

Two hours later, Todd stopped, and in half a minute, after the table lamp had been turned on, Neils rolled away. The photograph was still in Todd's hand, never having been put aside, I assumed. He brought the print to his chest and, taking its edges in both hands, admired it. "We will sleep now." He slung his legs and body from the bed. "Martin, you will be in need of a sleeping pill."

"I'd lik'un too," Neils chirped, pushing his body up with his elbows.

"You are not in need of one," he was told, and Neils slipped back, no argument.

I slept immediately, knowing I did not need the tablet I had taken. I woke up once, thinking I heard "dying voices"—Eliot's words, quoting another, I believe—coming from another room. I remember turning to the right and reaching out with hands and arms. "Todd . . . Hylas," I called out, although since my lips and tongue were swollen and anesthetized from kissing and suckling it could have come out "'Od . . . *Helas*," I pretty up my story by saying now. Whatever, the words brought me surcease from the emptiness of the bed's right side: "I am here," the voice said from just beyond the doorway. "Go back to sleep."

I did, consoled that I would have him for at least five weeks, and longer if the form the statue would take frustrated him. "Bulfinch, 'old father, old artificer,' your Scheherazade nights and works are over," I murmured.

Suddenly, I was conscious of a stream of light gushing over the room, but kept my eyes shut tight. My mind, aroused but just, began running through every scene I had ever read, certain it would land on one that he would accept for his next statue. "Marmeladov's wife," I cried out triumphantly, opening my eyes. "Marmeladov's wife, urging her children to—" I turned to tell him. I saw a pillow; it had been fluffed; the bottom sheet on his side also had been pulled taut.

The discovery that he was not there had to be whispered —barber-of-Midas-like—into some hole. I turned toward Neils' side. A folded-over rumpled pillow greeted me.

They're in the kitchen, taking breakfast, I told myself. Nice of them to let me sleep in. "Sleep in," I bolted upward. "My ten o'clock Renaissance poetry class!" I cried out toward the Citizen which showed fifteen to eleven. I grabbed the phone and dialed the Chair's office, made my excuse (with which I was satisfied), and felt a need to pee.

The neon light was prominent from the kitchen, so from the hallway, I called out, "I've missed my tenner." I looked in: Scattered across the formica top were two coffee cups and six beer cans (two crunched, so I knew on which side of the table Neils had sat).

"In the workroom," I affirmed, "already chiseling away." I delayed going for an uncertain time, finishing a cup of coffee, then some others—they had left the Royal plugged in. I tried to estimate how long it had brewed and told myself that I really shouldn't go in, disturbing him as he turned his myth into flesh. I crook'd an ear, intent on hearing the "tat-tat-tat" of Sculptor at Work.

I think (sometimes) I'm still crooking that ear.

3

Forty-three days later, the phone rang, after midnight, though come to think of it, for those one-and-a-half months every hour for me had been midnight.

"Neils's back. I sent him to the shower right away. God, how he smelled! Hylas must have dragged him through shit. All I gave him time to say was, 'Harold, I went with him to get him away from Martin.' Tomorrow you'll take him—fill in whatever 'off my/out of my' you want to. My piles are sleeping like a baby, and I intend for them to keep on snoring."

Here is what Neils said happened in New York:

It's him what take th'und'ed 'n' sev'nty two doll's yah billf'ld, a'und'ed what shoulda b' mine 'cause I eahn it. [Since I have grown accustomed to it, Neils' "gutter-al" English no longer grates on my otic nerves. Such is not your case: Therefore, the transcription of the remainder of his monologue may be regarded as a palimpsest, a plastering over—a bowdlerizing, if you please—of his phonetic and grammatical imperfections. (Cf. Shaw's argument in his *Pygmalion*.) A few of Neils' vulgarisms have been retained when they "charm" or approach malapropisms.] And the change from your pock't, an af'thought af' he wrote the note and put it in the freezer part of the frig. He knew you well, that you never take anything cold with ice till night.

[But that day I had, after I had finally gone to his workroom and verified that the Carrara was gone. The paper was stiffly frozen: "Gone to New York. You will not forget me. I would not be forgotten." So, I lost him *not* after he finished his sculpture, but before he began it, to explain the riddle I put above. I read it once, went to the phone, called the Chair, told him I was feeling better and would make my 1 o'clock. It was 20 to 1.]

The bus took 19 hours to New York, and I did all the food-getting. I had only $3.41 aft' I paid the $19 for the room and depos't. Not once did he go for his pock't. In Haiti Harlem it was—a bed, a sink, and a night table, no win'ow. I didn't mind. I'd got him that far from you, and had to stick 'round only to make sure he didn't come back. [Neils sighed at his sacrifice, glancing up to see if I had taken note.]

"I'll have to have a better table," he said, setting the canvas bag with the marble on the bed—I was carrying the one with his tools— and curling up beside it, "as sturdy as a meat butcher's block."

I sat down at the end of the bed, bemused. "None of that," he moved his foot which my left buttock had touched, "you've got to get to work."

"Work? I got no trade," I gruffed. You know that, Martin; I never worked. My Sister Mary, others, Harold, then you—'spec'ly you—took care of me. I wouldn't know how to work.

"There's a gay cinema four blocks down I saw coming in. I'll sculpt from noon to 8 and 8:15 to 4; so I'll need some food at 11:45 and at 8; at 4 bring me a bedtime snack."

"I never done no cin'ma sex!" I protes'd when he gave me time to.

"It'll be easy for you." He had taken his eyes off the canvas bag. "You're only to let them suck you. Nothing else."

I couldn't take the chance—him walking out and heading for the bus station. Back to you, and me with $3.41 in my pock't, and not even that a moment later. "Put the money you got on the table. I'll need it for the sculpting block. You better get going."

"Well give me time to wash up, put a shine on the merch'-dise," I said mean-like. I started to open his—your— suitcase.

"They'll like you the way you are."

I 'member and said at the door, "I'll need some money for the movie."

"I saw an alley next to it. You can scrounge up three bucks there. Back at 8 sharp."

He was lying on the bed, same place and position, when I returned, except now he was naked, all naked. Also, there was a stout table—it looked custom-made—covering most of the room beyond the bed. I don't know how he got it in the door, unless he had him who done it do it there. On it was the marble.

I guess it was the marble 'cause a red-and-white shirt was draped over. [One I had bought him. I felt flattered, but in the five times Neils narrated, I never once interrupted, as I am doing now, to give a sign I was.]

I knew he'd ask for it, so I 'ready had it in my right hand—the $22 I took in, two's, three's, and four's at a shot. [Neils looked guiltily at me, hoping to make me feel guilty. I didn't. I don't.] I ate something called a bagel with sou'cream, and he did too, with a coke. Never complained at what I picked out. Fifteen minutes later I knew it was time to exit, not both'ring to ask for money to get back in the movie. I didn't want to hear again the way he said "scrounge."

Four a.m., again he was lying on the bed, *sex nat'rale*. (You taught me them for'n words, Martin.) [Neils smiled broadly every time, bringing his downcast eyes up before letting them fall.] We ate in the dark, aft' I had put the $43 I'd tak'n in—"Got an out-of-towner for $10," I told him, perhaps sounding too proud—on the bed. No more talking by me, and none by him. Then I heard teeth splittin' op'n a rubb'rs pack't and . . . ."

["Of course, you did," I thought the first time Neils' voice trailed off. "A Sculptural Symmetry had to be maintained. Withers' began with the hand and closed with the mouth; mine opened with the mouth and closed with the ass; yours had to begin with the ass." But how would Neils' end? "Your story takes on some perking interest," I thought the first time.]

It was like that the next thirty-one days. Chunks first, then dust from the marble 'cum'la'd [accumulated] on top the table and on the floor. Something diff'rent happened the 33rd. The bulb was on when I came in. After he had eaten, he didn't tear open the rubb'r right away. Instead he took my cock and stuck his face next to it.

"'Cou'se it's a lil pink'n'blue," I grunted. "Yahs'd be too, it be gumm'd and chaw'd av'age 14 timesa day 33 days." [Neils always paused here and seemed to try to do the multiplication to get the grand total, but each time gave up.] I wasn't so foolish to think he was concerned about my cock's lab'rs, so I re'sured him, "Bu' th' skin's na'e b'ok'. I tell eachun 'fo'e he 'gins, 'Yah nickme 'n' I'll mak' yah th' chewin' gum 'low yah seat.' He dropped my cock, drew back his head, and looked toward the marble. Then I knew: He was doing my—Antaeus's—cock the next day. [He pronounced it "An'us" throughout.]

After he da-da-da'ed me, I couldn't sleep. It must have been almost finished. Which way would he go? I'm left in New York, and he's back in West Palm gifting you the statue. Six days later, I knew I had been guttered. Bag'ls in hand, I tried the door at 8. Locked. I rattled it. Still locked. I sat down on the top step of the stairs and burr'ed [burrowed] my head in my hands, the right one still clutching like a bunch of fl'ers the $26 I had hard-earned sin' noon.

Martin, it's the truth, I thought not of me having been guttered by him and not of nineteen or so hours later when he would be back with you and you back with him, but of you and me when we were 'gether, 'fore he came. That day on the by-path in Meadah Park when you tried to take my hand as we walked through the pink-'n'-blue fl'er garden and I shook you off. And that mem'ry must have—like mother's milk—made me sleep.

The money was being slid from my hand. I 'woke. He was standing over me. Dressed in an el'gant charcoa' black silk suit and a fancy tie and the red-and-white shirt. "Everything's arranged. You'll need a suit and other things. Four doors from the cinema, there's a clothing store run by gays." He pushed four connec'd cel'phane packs of rubb'rs into my hand. "But the clerks are not to bugger you." He had taken the bag of two bag'ls and was biting into one. "Bring me back my condoms if they have their own."

When I returned—new clothes and shoes on—I foll'ed his stare toward the table. The marble was now covered with the canvas bag, newly washed and pressed.

Next morning we took a bus far uptown from where we were, then walked four blocks before we stopped in front of a wind'less stonefront. It had a tiny door of gold-fringed metal. We entered, stepped up three times and moved toward a desk. The young, almost-young, man sitting there took his time looking up, but once he did, and his eyes landed on Hylas—I don't even think he saw me—he smiled till I thought his face was all a smile, like that Chesh'r' cat. "Can I please help you?"

"Monsieur Malimerde, please. [The "i" was elided by Neils.] I'm a sculptor." He held up the canvas bag. "Todd Hylas." He put a 'termi'te stress on his last name.

The deskguy fiddled for the handle of the tel'phone and then for a button on it. "Daniel, a M. Todd Hylas, the sculptor, is here to see you." A pause. "Oh, I think you'll want to bring him into your lions' den, most definitely. Did I say sculptor or Greek statue?" I was certain he didn't see me 'cause, aft' Hylas had been let pass, he 'most closed the door on me.

The man I took for M. Mal'merde had a thick, pumped-up mass of hair or a good wig, was in his middle fifties, with gold-rimmed glasses. He was hunched over a desk twice the size of the one in the other room. Looked short. He glanced up, and his body quickly foll'd his rising eyelids.

Hylas walked with a deb'nair strut toward the desk and plopped the canvas bag on it. "I have one of my marbles to sell"—as if there's more than one, the hyp'crite. M. Mal'merde had already sat back down. He brought his hands to his chin, making a gabl', and nodded his head toward the bag, but did not take his eyes from Hylas' face.

This was the first time I had seen it, Martin. I will say this: He got me right.

He bent down to line it up. I saw M. Mal'merde's eyes were tracking him. At first they seemed to be searching for Hylas' face behind it, but when Hylas rose, his were still fixed on the facsim'e of me and him. "It's called 'Antaeus Uplifted.' You know the myth: Hercules [pronounced as expected "He'c'les"] and Antaeus, the son of Earth. I think one—several—of your clients might be interested in it." M. Mal'merde's right hand reached across the desk and began to stroke the left shoulder of Hylas—Hylas *in* the statue. He was no longer looking at the 'rig'nal.

"You must give me some references. I cannot make an offer without some verifying references," he mumbled with a stammer.

"I have none. Just my statue."

"But it may be stolen." His voice suggest'd to me that he wanted, really wanted, to be 'comm'da'ng [accommodating]. "If it's your first, just the telephone number of an art teacher."

"There are some other agents who specialize in statues of this ilk," Hylas answered. [Neils pronounced the word as "elk."] But he did not move to take the statue in hand. "The penis tucked under the chin's a nice touch. Here's the print I worked from." He tossed the Pol'roid phot'graph onto the desk.

M. Mal'merde studied it closely, holding it in his left hand, his other not having ceased off fondling the statue. "This verifies you were the model"—it was like I did not exist—"but not that you were the sculptor." Hylas reached forward, brushed M. Mal'-merde's hand away, placed his on the facsim'e of my face, but made not a motion of bagging the statue.

"I'll give you $500." M. Mal'merde circled his fly-swatted right hand 'round the statue and placed—re-placed—it just below Hylas' butt. With both having slapped hands on it, it was just like two capt'ns using a ball bat to 'termine which team would be in first.

"The Carrara alone cost $700."

As they cont'nued to higgle, I noticed that M. Mal'merde was inching upward and inward his rubbing fingers.

At "My final offer's $2300," Hylas ripped the statue toward him, leaving M. Mal'merde's hand atwitch in air. He shook the canvas bag open. "No more of your thirty-pieces-of-silver offers. I need $5000, and that *is* final." A crook'd smile came to his face. "I wager if I put my statue down and brought my right hand to your penis, I would find it as hard as this one in marble."

He'd clasped it so his hand was over mine, *in* the statue. "I have researched your special clientele. What would one—several—of them give—$10,000, $20,000—to get by means of a glance— immediately, eternally, and all his own—what pulsatingly pushes now at the inseams of your trousers?" [Sickening, isn't it, what rhetorical apotheosizing will do to one's syntax?]

M. Mal'merde slumped back. "You'll take a check?"

"No."

It was agreed his sec'tar' would step 'round the corner to withdraw the $5000. "*Bon,*" Hylas smiled. "That'll give me time to do the last bit." The statue was turned over to its und'side, and having taken a flat chis'l and a small mall't out of the bag I was carrying, he knelt and began to tap: "Tat-tat-tat." ["I hear! I hear!" I artificially shouted to myself, the first time.] Even in that squat, neither his body nor his hand shook as he s'rated a vert'cal line, a second an inch or so away, and then a 'nectin' di'g'nal: "H."

I stepped back not wanting to see th'other letters, knowing my sig'ture wouldn't be there, though it was through me, the sweat of my cock, the statue was birthed. M. Mal'merde rounded the desk, his eyes alt'nate' on Hylas' body and face and the work of his hands. The bending, and perhaps simply being in 'ration [adoration, I presume] before his statue, had puffed up the muscles of Hylas' body and put a rad'ance on his face. I saw M. Mal'merde had also engath'ed his body, but like a frog's, ready to spring from a lil'pad to snag a fly.

I should have expect'd what came next—'memb'ring what he did to you after he saw the Pol'roid—but must admit I was surprised. Hylas pushed up slightly, unzipped his pants and took out his cock, on half-hard I saw. He glanced toward the taut M. Mal'merde: "You can tongue it while I sculpt, if you want."

He was still in the room when I got back that night at 8. (When he insist'd, after we stepped from the building, that I go about my cin'ma bus'ness, I was sure I would be welcomed by a locked door.) He took the bottle of coke and ope'ly dropped the three tablets in it, saying "A Good Night's Sleep for you." I lay next to him. His hand came over and fell onto my cock.

Martin, you know how bigg'r 'un av'rage I am on soft. I swear *at* his touch, mine 'ginned to 'tract up. He fiddled with a rubb'r, but my cock had sunk so inside me he finely settled for draping it over what was left of my nuts, and rolled over onto his belly. I went through the motions of shoving against him. It was him what found the rubb'r slipped away, and tucked it in his asshole. I humped, quite certain that in his mind I was being let to enter him. [My interest got its perk, *which* I should have foreseen.]

Martin, it was like in making himself 'vail'ble to me he was serving up the last supper to a condemn'd pris'ner.

I didn't sleep, though I kept my eyes shut. Foll'd ment'lly his ev'ry movement the next morning. Kept them tight even when I heard him going through my pock'ts, looking for change I might have held back. Still with my eyes covered by my eyelids, like a deadman's coins over them, when I was certain he was at the door, I bespoke, "Whehta now?"

No answer, not with words. I waited two hours 'fore I walked to the butcher's block. What I read in the gristle of the marble brought me to my knees; tears fell onto my hard'ning cock, which rose 'n' rose like unto a prayer to Heaven: "Gonta Rome. Yah'll not f'hge' me. I not be f'hgo'n." [Neils slurred here.] M' f'hty-day wild'ness was ove'.

4

Today we are at Riviera Beach beach. Although it is only a little after 9, the sand is already mostly hidden by sunbathers, convincing me that much of Greater West Palm is playing a guilty, sinful hooky from church this Easter Sunday. Allowing for time differences between Florida and Italy, I know the Pope is making his way to the balcony of St. Peter's to sprinkle Christ-uplifted blessings on the afternoon faithful, many of whom (being tourists) will be clutching plaster of Paris statuettes of Our Saviour.

I am diddling with a poem I had mostly finished last night while I was buggering Neils ("This boy is transportation / On which I hitch my ride.") He had come into what was now my study (Neils himself had torn up all of "*his* stone" and restored the room to pinewood), dragging me away from the *Loci* of Philipp Melanchthon, Martin Luther's—my German name-sake's—acolyte. I was reading the copy at hand, Melanchthon's own German translation of his Late Medieval Latin original. And having difficulty, perhaps as much as Melanchthon had in making the translation into a tongue, though his native, in which he wrote like a barbarian.

But no-one has ever written better about self-love than he, so I was persevering in his transubstantiation commentary, until called away "by a greater love" (Melanchthon's words): Neils' coaxing me away "to hitch a [femural] ride" on his back. For certain, in this world, where man is "bespoke to die," "surety" is paradoxically "ephemeral."

I cross out the word "bread-wine" and write over it, "giblets." Why? Because when Harold, Neils, and I had stopped at Ho-Jo's this morning for a pre-beach breakfast, Neils had ordered chicken giblets on American toast. Furthermore, the transubstan-tiation controversy which had so obsessed Herr Melanchthon is suggested by the previously-cited "transportation." You don't

want to overdo anything in a poem, except the meter. I write the
title now: "Three Puns: Written After Being interrupted While
Reading Melanchthon's *Loci*."

The pompous title reminds me to check that the puns—Don't
want to be wrong in my count!—exceed not a trinity: 1st stanza,
"th'ephemeral" / "the femural," Neils' fleshy thighs around mine
for a time. 2nd stanza: "I little rate" [what "the totem Terror tells
me"] / "alliterate," the letters of Melanchthon's The Word, since
soul, as well as flesh, must have its say. 3rd stanza: "[For Man
shall] die a dim [death]" / "diadem"; the Spirit which the German
says joins flesh and soul calls forth not only Christ's crown of
thorns, but also the circular thatch about Neils' asshole.

"Without that Spirit," I protest now as in the poem, "damn
it, we are all left 'With Breath, hung out and dried.'"

Of course, it must be asked, "Where is *he* in all of this?"
Harold is adamant: "To get to his 'beyond–God,–Todd,' he had
to destroy us, gutter us all—Father, Son, and Holy Ghost. I—the
Father—as The Word ('and the Word was God'), for from me he
took only Words. You—the Son—for were you not crucified that
night he, probably kicking aside the dropped Polaroid, tossed
you onto the bed, in the center of Golgotha's sinners, and did
not you yourself say you descended into an abyss? And poor
Neils, like our Holy Ghost, unhoused from Heaven, doomed for
eternity to be dragged through the shit of this world." He paused,
panting and bereft of breath.

For sure, I didn't, and don't, necessarily disagree with Harold,
but do believe his interpretation does necessarily limit Hylas.
Why not see the relationships artistically, as technique, ideology,
and execution? Or physically as mass, mach 1, mach 2: e (Hylas)
$= m$ (Harold), c squared (myself and Neils)? Or, since Withers has
a religious turn of mind, evolutionarily: The Old Man (Adam) sins
into the New Man (Christ) who crucifies himself to become
Anti-Man/-Christ, Yeats' (and Goya's) "rough beast" "slouching

towards Bethlehem," but in our case "flown to Rome."

At that time and place, I remember I protested to the exasperated Withers. "O Herald," I punned, "but were any of us destroyed? Guttered, yes, but destroyed?" The rhetorical question made Withers gasp the more. "I can't be so sure we weren't. Surety for sure is ephemeral," and so you see not all the images of my poem come from Melanchthon.

"I am slinking towards celibacy, . . . transubstantiating," at Ho-Jo's Harold had whispered to me, out of the earshot of Neils, this Easter Morning. A few minutes ago, as if to prove his point, he returned from walking the beach and growled, disdainful of the available young men, "I saw nothing to turn my head, but much to turn my stomach." He is sleeping now, with a snore, a golf cap crook'd over his eyes, forehead and bald spot.

Beyond what *he* is and what *he* got from us, what did we get from *him*, other than that he had less self-love, using Melanchthon's definition, than any of us? I can speak solely for myself, of course. I have learned not only to accept the imperfections of this world, this life, but also to luxuriate in that imperfection.

Enough.

I glance from the poem—which I am even now ripping up (as *he* three times did) and letting its tatters be caught as litter by the sea breeze—towards Neils, who at the water's edge, has made an opening, and is engaged in his calisthenics. The tough pliancy of his body has been whipped to what I would call an Abstract ideal.

He sees me looking at him; his lips turn up a mischievous smile. He cups his left hand over the index finger of his right, pointing downward, as if to hide his code from the others on the beach. My eyes are directed toward his sig'ture: there is barely an imprint being made by his penis on the pink-'n'-blue surface of the bikini. His body falls forward, and on the sand, never taking his eyes from me, he begins his push-ups, stopping at 33. The smile never leaves his face, and when he arises, the haloed finger again slyly points.

The bulge is such that it threatens to break the bounds of the stretch-cotton. He begins to pace toward me, a bestriding Antony, his plumage spreading even more, at a speed beyond that of mass and light, time and place.

I am content, or so I tell myself.

Damn it! How can you "not forget" someone who has no memory of even being there with you? He will not have forgotten me since I was never present to be forgotten. And so I suppose I must remember him because, in a transubstantiating sense, he *hasn't* forgotten me.

My eyes have drifted beyond the swollen shoulders of the approaching Neils. In a mass of over-the-sea clouds, as dense and jismic and effulgent as marble, I see him. Somehow he has gotten into St. Peter's; the papal procession, a second before symmetrically making its way toward the balcony, is of course frozen, for at the Still Point only *he* moves. His head is leaning forward, transversing the narrow slot between the uniformed bodies of the Swiss guards, and edges toward the ear of Pope John.

In Late Medieval Latin as perfect as Melanchthon's, he whispers, the question all rhetorical, "Got any chapels you need painted?"

APPENDIX

Editor's Note: We have surreptitiously obtained a copy of the poem, "Three Puns, etc.," and print the doggerel, not wishing to leave a void in our readers' mind:

> *When soul stunts flesh (vice versa)*
> *—The crossfire stuns my sleep!—*
> *Roused is th'ephemeral surety*
> *That man should scorn to weep*
> *For Man, born to weep.*
>
> *That totem Terror tells me*
> *—I little rate the lie—*
> *"Oh, man can choke on giblets,*
> *But cannot choke the cry*
> *For Man, bespoke to die."*
>
> *This boy is transportation*
> *—On which I hitch my ride—*
> *"For man shall die a dim death,"*
> *The spirited ones deride,*
> *"With Breath, hung out and dried."*

UPON SHAKESPEARE'S COUCH

WT: Let us assume, for this poem, you were
          queer, William Shakespeare, better did prefer
          the fair young friend to the mistress black,
          then I can lie upon your couch—

WS: "And talk!"
          Your rhymes are slant; and you would make me Freud
          (As if he'd not done that enough). You've scanned
          My sonnets; now my person's played on, toyed
          With, a pensioned metaphor, on command
          Invoked and curtained to the stage you've set:
          Backdrop, framework. But at the back who's framed?
          Not I! Go seek out long-eared Lyly or get
          Raleigh, a captive audience, or have tamed
          Marlowe, now there's a chap more of—

WT: "[My] ilk."
          Break off your sonnet, Shakespeare. I would talk.

A. TYRANTS AND DARK SURVEYORS

Those black eyes cut
down to a servant's size
the black night. Day holds some
in check, stars and the vacant
cat on the windowsill,
which night-slashed become
dark surveyor and tyrant.

There is death in his eyes,
but no decay, ever the cat.
I see him—Dino—
his black eyes torn
from the discotheque dance,
mornings found still,
dry as soot,
condescending no glance
at the dawn.

B. THE DOPE BOY

How can there be so much
careless venom in your body
that if I move right or left am struck
by the darling fangs of a baby?

We are saturated: all's needed
is a cut and the acid spurts.
I have sucked crack and the dope boy
and awakened with a gut full of poison.

If you think you are not phallin, Ace,
think again. The fang-marks of your needle
scar my arms, and this knotted body and mind
you see were once a tree which fed the air.

A'. MAUDLIN

I have seen men away from wife or girlfriend
grow maudlin: "I am going to make 50 grand—"
an emphatic pause, "for Paulette!"
my future brother-in-law, thick-tongued on two beers,
declaimed to the four of us gathered around an army bunk.
That was three years ago.
The other two, married, nodded assent, passing around
     encouragement,
Hurrahs! for "the silliest thing ever said."
And their eyes wore a longing—I thought
it "maudlin" and wanted to crush it with a taunt.
No-one wanted to go to an empty bed, even me,
who thought them ridiculous
that could not take a two-week
leave from house and spouse manfully.

Tonight, far from Dino, come in
from drinking beers with well-mates, husbands
trapped in this university town and dorm, who began the
     night at the first bar
ogling the girls with eye and mouth, and now drag in,
     sloppy in their
talk of wife and children.
I accept every word, while they try
to excuse their feelings, "You can't understand,
Bill, not married, and that baby's a regular

princess . . . ." How stuck deep am I by the bonds
that turn men's after-bar talk into the deep-struck!
Tonight, far
from Dino,
the word *maudlin*
taunts me and will not let me sleep.

B': RICH NECTAR

How does my heart still beat
blood through my hands and feet
and through my loins send stream
now that the boy is gone?

Amazing body that won't break
when the mind begins to quake,
but will eat and rest and shit,
content to make the dead quick.

Spirit and body both bleed
rich nectar on the battlefield;
loins and heart drop their load:
is Boy Ace quick or dead?

C. IN RAW VERSE

I could hardly wait, after a night
when we had argued through a game
of ping-pong, wild slam
accenting point after point,
to get Larry down, as he was that night, in raw verse.

This year coming home to a room
empty-handed, having leveled a night,
I write I can go to bed or write,
the pen in my hand, scratching and hacking,
before I know it, words for a poem I don't feel like making.

D. A PENNY

How do we stand
in this gravitated world?

Everyone who enters his room
must drop, he says, a penny into
a twisted beer can
("My cover charge").
Why do I hear copper clink
on aluminium,
not copper?

He dreams of a boat and has put $200
in the bank, and tries to lure
what money he thinks I have
into his dream.
He draws me forward,
then withdraws,
but when I move to leave,
whines and calls me back.
(All nods and smiles,
I speak perhaps twice in the two hours, for I am drawn
by his French accent, need to hear it
as he needs someone to listen.)
"I would fuck you if you were a girl,"
Roc giggles.

All is physics,
a calculus of relations.

Somehow we stand
in this gravitated world.

C'. DOG-AND-CAT PASSION

What dog–and–cat moments we had,
Larry and I! And then he woke,
saw what he had done, had become, shook
with indignation, rolled from the bed
and never spoke to me again. How simple simple passion is,
dog-and-cat passion! That hot sliver of penis
trembles, and there is a hurt look
in his and his bitch's eyes,
but spent, they untangle, and trot
off, in their eyes not a glint of guilt.

D'. BABY-FAT

In thrall to a 19-year-old punk,
baby-fat dripping from his cheeks.
He dabbles in construction, but not enough
to pink-tan his neck. Hulking,
I am the whale which throws itself
on the beach to choke in the sand.
I went to Roc tonight, firmed
that he would do as I bid.
But he was young, going to Miami,
and slammed the door
in passing me by.
Left me shaky.

E. FAGOT IN RESERVE

Diogenes, stick
young candle
into the heart of Jim,
him I would have sworn
upon, or into my own heart,
but before, be sure, old man,
you have another fagot.

F. DO ANGELS GOSSIP AT GOD'S THRONE?

Limit me to one word, and I
shall be silent, for someone must
need my word for me to speak.
Given Roger, I could have made
a dictionary with your one word,
but shall be silent.
And if you think this boy has
left me speechless, perhaps
he was the word you gave me.

E'. "HE, WHO GUIDES . . ."

The sniper prepares to pick me off;
I stare into the muzzle of Jim's rifle
and wish him luck.
For final seconds, I count pigeons preening,
until the vision quivers,
quivers as the telephone line
where they testily perch—

Had I such balance, my sight would zero in,
the assassin's bullet would not pass me by—
One, two, 3, 4, 5, 6 pigeons fly:
Not one hits me.

F'. WHAT IS LIFE?

Metronomically leading to midnight
and beyond, Roger—expectant
as the second
that I count, that I confront,
knowing that the next, no longer definite,
will confound me—thrusts, gets his fill,
a metronome to midnight and beyond.

A triple weight is death:
A magic blow, a sudden fall,
and breath in flight.

G. "WAS GREECE":
PLATO AND THE CHISELED PENISES

"The great Greek statuary? It is found
in Omonia Square, the gay bars of Plaka.
The other"—he spoke with conceit, perhaps selfless conceit,
as if he had exhausted many years learning
beauty cannot be bound up in art,
art cannot circumscribe beauty— "statuary, have you noticed
how gingerly they chiseled away the penises. I am sure
the craftsmen of the monastery hid each stone-hard cock
under his pillow, . . . dreaming, . . . wetly dreaming."
I caught him catching me as my eyes followed a red-shirted

young man, with a soldier's haircut, moving in circles
around the bar. Apologetically I said,
"They are all so beautiful." He translated with a laugh
to the statue we had picked up.
The statue spoke some Greek to him. He laughed again,
"Stephanos says, 'Yes, but they all have complexes.'"
I thought a moment, while he laughed a third time.
"But beauty should be complex." I considered
the young man I had seen last night,
with so many shades of contempt in his mouth
I'd not had time to study his eyes.
"But not art," I would have riposted, but he didn't.
"The church did queer things to Greece,
more than just chopping off penises."
(Plato did it first. He killed Greece,
but I didn't add that, not wanting to complicate things.)
My Nestor again, "We are the queer ones,
Bill, and have no right to make complex
a simple country and a simple church."
I was not so sure, but again kept back.
Wayne cleared his throat (*bon mot* time:
he'll exhaust all he has on this my second night with him
in Athens): "The glory that is Greece is in its boys."
He squeezed the statue. "Thank God, this one's
has not been chiseled away. Thank God through his church."
The statue, understanding nothing, mimed a certain *sang-froid*,
its lineage dating to the Age of Pericles.
(Stingy *hubris* held back the Persians at Thermopylae,
the same that gave me everything
in bed last night but a kiss.)
"I would like the red one"—I was also at the point of exhaustion
and was inclined to believe
what Plato had to say c. 2500 years ago,

tonight he repeated word for word in his stony stride—
"the next time he comes around."

G'. "WAS ROME": ANGELO AND HIS NUDES

Tommaso snores. You grudge the boy his sleep.
Had not you felt for him, all day stroking
among the cold slab for his form, your youth, fresh
up from Florence and come to be pampered
into stone, but could not beat his flesh into marble?

Nothing comes impatiently. His body,
quirk-some in bed as the formless marble, shakes
from your artist hands, evades. You're sure
he thinks, as you move to touch, "Must I endure
his calloused fists stroking my buttocks into stone?"

Flesh is bitter—That's why you work
in marble. Finally you sleep, and in a nightmare
are an eagle and are the pumiced form
it falls upon, answering, "Why cannot those
we touch understand what love goes into our art?"

But you got both, old man. Cavalieri
climbed from your bed, yet another David.
Both: but there is a face, Saint-held apart,
formless Sistine skin, an old man's. Dying, did
he wish he had not etched an eternity into his art?

WS: Your revels now are ended, I assume.
        Shall you or I first hasten from this room?
        I'll grant you this, before I ghostly fly:
        Love is in truth a self-inflicted lie.
        Lie on your couch, not mine—

WT: I never lied, to myself, except
           that time, and that time before.
           And can I lie, to myself, again,
           be tripped up by truth once more?
           You would have a truth and a lie:
           I gave you both.
           Which did not satisfy?
           We've played our lying roles. I kept
           to yours, you kept to mine,
           up until truth became both Player Booth
           and Honest Abe, Sly
           Oswald and Slyer JFK. And I am left
           to lie with truth.

WS: I'll let you lie.

AN ANTI-ELEGY FOR AUDEN

Nothing in his life
so barnacling as his poems:
Took to wife
a Mann, oft slept at others' homes,
remembered by one host
for a cigarette burn
left not just on an armrest,
but a rare piano.
("Doesn't affect the tone,"
his voice chirped, Rococo.)
Such wit drolls monotonously
in resentment of life as foible;
it becomes static, hollow,
edgy: Like his Romantic campaign
for Oxford residency,
and the Nobel.
Better to skip to his letting go.
Certes, he came to Vienna
to take in the opera,
not to die:
His final digs, a room in a cheap hotel.
Even that he justified, man to man, as economical:
"Walking distance, to the music," spoke' with a Baroque sigh.
(Economy being Life's *desideratum*.)
Left unsaid—the minion of his poetic techniques—
was that the better *hoteliers* forbade
the taking up of peripatetic tricks
from the nearby Renaissance square.
There, behind an inside-locked door,
he paused and died.
Not exactly an operatic climax,
more a poetic mirror.
Poetry sticks.

The author, William Tarvin,
a retired professor of English
literature, has published
articles in Modern Language
Quarterly, Journal of Reading,
Essays in Literature, and other
scholarly journals.

He taught in Saudi Arabia
(the setting of The Saint of
Sodomy) for seventeen years.

GLB FICTION

The Bunny Book   US $11.95   ——
Novel by **John D'Hondt**

A Classic of literature that deals with AIDS...   – Robert Glück

Snapshots For A Serial Killer   US $10.95   ——
Fiction and Play by **Robert Peters**

Beautiful, layered, taut, weird, surprising...   – Dennis Cooper

Zapped: Two Novellas   US $11.95   ——
Two Novellas by **Robert Peters**

Comic book gestalt, as featured in *Atom Mind*.

The Devil In Men's Dreams   US $11.95   ——
Short Stories by **Tom Scott**

Sentiments from humor to remorse...   – Lambda Book Report

White Sambo   US $12.95   ——
Novel in stories by **Robert Burdette Sweet**

Powerful and touching vision of gay life...   – Shelby Steele

A Time To Live   US $ 13.95   ——
Novel by **Jim Brogan**

Embraces the intrigue of reality itself.   – Robert Burdette Sweet

Unruly Angels   US $14.95   ——
Novel by **Ronald Nevans**

A gemlike, thoroughly accomplished novel.   – Felice Picano

Different Voices   US $12.95   ——
A Different Voice and Other Stories by **Walter Febick**

Captures the essence of sexually-confused young men.– Jim Brogan

ADD $2.50 PER BOOK FOR SHIPPING/HANDLING (US)   ——
Send Check or money order to:

                    GLB PUBLISHERS   **TOTAL**   ____
          P.O. Box 78212, San Francisco, CA 94107

Mail to: _____

_____

Look for us on the Web! **www.glbpubs.com**

EXPLICIT GAY FICTION
FROM G**L**B PUBLISHERS

POETRY FROM
GLB PUBLISHERS

A BREVIARY OF TORMENT
Poems by **Thomas Cashet**   US $ 13.95   _____

*Erudite, witty and mordant, fascinating in its
repulsiveness and ever-so-delicate in its graphic excess.*
— Felice Picano

GOOD NIGHT, PAUL
Poems by **Robert Peters**   US $ 8.95   _____

*This is some of Peters' most personal and reveal-
ing work, and belongs in the library of every poet.*
— Dumars Reviews

KINGS AND BEGGARS
Poems by **Paul Genega**   US $ 9.95   _____

*Paul Genega is rapidly distinguishing himself as a
major voice in contemporary American poetry.*
— William Packard

THE WEIGH-IN
Collected Poems of **Winthrop Smith**   US $ 12.95   _____

*There is an ecstasy here, and an incantatory
voice, wonderully erotic in the way they explore the
many locales of male sexual migrations.*
— The James White Review

SUBWAY STOPS
Collected Poems of **Abnorman**   US $ 11.95   _____

*Abnorman's poems, joyous and brave, reverber-
ate with originality and zest. They steam and scream
with a no-nonsense style.*   — Robert Peters

ADD $2.50 FOR EACH BOOK FOR SHIPPING/HANDLING   _____
(US Only)
Send Check or Money Order to: TOTAL   _____

GLB PUBLISHERS
P.O. Box 78212, San Francisco, CA 94107

Mail to _____

_____

Look for us on the Web! **www.glbpubs.com**